No. 5 / The Life of Yeasts

The Life of Yeasts

THEIR NATURE, ACTIVITY, ECOLOGY,
AND RELATION TO MANKIND

H. J. PHAFF, M. W. MILLER, E. M. MRAK

HARVARD UNIVERSITY PRESS

CAMBRIDGE, MASSACHUSETTS

Preface

The present monograph was written with the belief that there is a need for information on yeasts to serve the nonspecialist who occasionally comes in contact with this group of microorganisms and who wishes to orient himself further without resorting to the use of complex treatises written mainly for the specialist.

In most colleges and universities yeasts are considered in less than a single lecture of elementary bacteriology or biology courses, and in more advanced mycology courses only two or three periods may be devoted to these organisms. However, even mycology courses are by no means a standard part of the curricula for Ph.D. candidates in microbiology or other branches of the biological sciences. Yet many biological chemists, geneticists, and other scientists use yeasts as tools in their work because of the suitability of these organisms for studies on cell biology and physiology. Perhaps because of their availability, nearly all of such studies have been done with baker's or brewer's yeast (*Saccharomyces cerevisiae* and *S. carlsbergensis*) and to a lesser extent with feed or torula yeast (*Candida utilis*). A more important reason, however, is that most biologists and biochemists have little familiarity with the vast array of yeast species known today and with their fascinating diversity in metabolic, biochemical, nutritional, and genetic properties.

It is our hope that the brief contents of this book may help to orient those who wish to obtain simple answers to questions pertaining to the life of yeasts.

Some may wonder whether there is a need for a monograph written neither from the popular nor the very technical point of view. Disregarding the classical literature on yeast, which has mainly historical significance, we believe that current books on the subject are either too lengthy for the casual explorer in the domain of yeasts, or that emphasis is unduly heavy on the biochemical and physiological activities. Moreover, much information, especially that pertaining to ecology and general biology of yeasts, is available only in the form of research publications in technical journals. We have tried to offer a reasonably balanced series of topics, covering the vital activities of yeast, somewhat de-emphasizing general biochemical aspects and metabolic pathways (which are found in all standard textbooks), while placing somewhat greater emphasis on certain biological properties.

Taxonomic information cannot be covered adequately in a short space and is likely to be of least interest to the nonspecialist. The treatment of this area, therefore, is minimized and placed at the end of the monograph as a brief introduction to the subject, covering the principles used in yeast classification, followed by somewhat abbreviated descriptions or diagnoses of the various yeast genera, and a very brief alphabetical listing of the genera in tabular form. We felt that the latter was necessary, for in discussing morphological, physiological, ecological, and other features of yeasts, it is necessary to give examples of species belonging to certain genera with which the reader may not be familiar. A quick reference to the diagnoses therefore helps to clarify their main characteristics.

In the opening chapter we have discussed concepts of yeast

from the time they were first observed to the present. Then follows a disscussion of the morphology of yeast cells and of the ways in which they propagate vegetatively or asexually. This is followed by a consideration of the cytology of yeast cells, including cell envelope and internal structures. The next two chapters deal with the sexual reproduction through the formation of ascospores, and the use which has been made of the discovery of a sexual cycle in yeast in introducing genetic studies. As mentioned earlier, information on metabolic activities is primarily directed toward pointing out lesser-known characteristics of yeast rather than repeating the well-known metabolic pathways. In the chapter on nutrition, standard growth requirements are discussed, and this is followed by examples of yeasts which are particularly demanding and which must be supplied with special nutrients or environments in order to grow. Ecological information, that is, the conditions under which yeasts actually live and propagate in nature, is covered in more detail because it is normally least understood by the nonspecialist. Yeast as food spoilage organisms, a special aspect of ecology, is treated in a separate chapter. This is followed by an account of the uses which have been made of yeast in industry for the benefit of man. Then, as indicated earlier, a brief account of yeast taxonomy concludes the book.

We are glad to take this opportunity to express our appreciation to Mrs. Sylvia Nevins and Miss Ellen R. Barker for their help in preparing several of the illustrations, their careful proofreading of the manuscript, and for constructive criticisms. We hope that the contents of this brief treatise will provide some stimulation of interest in the yeasts, the group of microorganisms which has been a source of inspiration to the authors for many years.

H. J. P., M. W. M., E. M. M.

Contents

ILLUSTRATIONS

The Life of Yeasts

I / Historical Aspects

The word "yeast" immediately brings to mind fermentation, for the two terms have been closely associated throughout their histories. Though yeast was used before history began to be recorded, man was in complete ignorance of the nature of these organisms. This is well indicated by the fact that the term "yeast" as used in many languages is merely a description of its gross appearance or what it did for the ancients. The French term for yeast, *levure*, comes from the Latin *levere*, meaning to raise, which is connected with the evolution of carbon dioxide during fermentation, thus appearing to raise the surface of the liquid as a foam. The German *Hefe* comes from a stem *heben*, also meaning to lift. The English word "yeast" and the related word *gist* in Dutch are derived from the Greek term *zestos*, which means boiled—again a reference to the bubbling foam caused by the evolution of carbon dioxide during fermentation.

The fermentation of fruit juices, and more indirectly the extracts of cereal grains, by mixed populations of yeast probably constituted the first uses of yeast by mankind and resulted in types of alcoholic beverages which may be considered the forerunners of our present-day wine and beer. Even today, certain primitive tribes in Peru are known to pretreat cereal grains by chewing the kernels prior to fermentation to convert starch into fermentable sugar. It is easy to imagine the early incorporation of fermenting liquid into bread dough and hence the orgin of raised, or leavened, bread. Just when these practices of accidental origin were first discovered by mankind is a matter of speculation. That fermentations and bread-making were well established some 4000 years ago is graphically shown by models of a brewery and bakery found in an Egyptian tomb at Thebes on the Nile. The exodus of Moses and the Jews from Egypt, as related in the Bible, tells us of their use of unleavened bread, because in their haste to depart the leavening was left behind. Apparently all of the ancient civilizations utilized the products of fermentation very much as we do today.

The development of the concept of yeast *per se* is relatively recent and may be considered to have had its beginning with the recorded observations of van Leeuwenhoek in 1680 of tiny "animalcules." He observed a variety of minute, living things in droplets of various materials with the microscopes he had made as a hobby. In actuality the instrument with which he observed these very small bodies was not a microscope as we know it today, but rather a carefully hand-ground and polished lens, set between metal plates, which could be focused upon the object by moving the object toward the lens. Van Leeuwenhoek's microscopes were capable of magnifying objects only 250–270 times their natural size. Only by his extreme skill in grinding and polishing these lenses and his unusual perceptiveness was he able to discover microorganisms as small as yeasts.

One of the materials examined was a droplet of fermenting beer. The numerous yeast cells it contained he described as globular bodies, sometimes oval or spherical in shape. These first observations of yeast cells were recorded by van Leeuwenhoek as drawings and as descriptions in letters to members of the Royal Society of London. The significance of his findings, however, was not realized by his contemporaries, nor by those who followed immediately, for it was nearly 150 years later before additional information on yeast was forthcoming. The intervening century-and-a-half was taken up by the experiments of numerous proponents and opponents of the theory which claimed that living things could develop spontaneously.

The theory of spontaneous generation probably existed since man first gave thought to the orgin of living things. Aristotle in the fourth century B.C. asserted that animals could arise from different kinds of animals, from plants, or even soil. The influence of his concepts was still strongly felt as late as the seventeenth century. Experiments by Francesco Redi and other opponents of this theory helped to quell the idea as far as macroscopic animals were concerned. The discovery of the tiny "animalcules" by van Leeuwenhoek started arguments anew as to their origin. Needham in 1749 claimed they arose from meat, whereas Spallanzani shortly afterwards kept microorganisms from appearing in meat by boiling the meat for one hour and then sealing the flask in which it was cooked. Claims that air was vital to the spontaneous generation of microorganisms was subsequently disproved by Schulze and by Schwann in the early nineteenth century and by Schroeder and von Dusch about 1850. The former used air which was heated to high temperatures; the latter used cotton plugs to filter the air which was allowed to enter flasks of heated meat extract. These two treatments prevented the development of microbes in sterilized broth. Such experiments designed to disprove spontaneous generation essentially ended with Pasteur's work in 1864 when he used flasks with long, thin necks curved into a gooseneck shape. In such a flask air could pass into the flask without obstruction, but particles and germs in the air impinged upon the walls of the neck and did not gain access to the broth where they might multiply. Tyndall supplemented these experiments by showing that dust carried germs, and if the air was dust-free no growth of organisms would occur.

Knowledge gained during the early and middle part of the nineteenth century served as a basis for several modern fields of biological science. Present-day biochemists, physiologists, and nutritionists all have an interest in the discovery that fermentation is the consequence of yeast's vital activities. The view expressed by Erxleben in 1818, that yeast consisted of living vegetative organisms responsible for fermentation, received little attention at that time. New interest in this view was stimulated some years later by Cagniard de la Tour in France (1835) and by Schwann and Kützing (1837) in Germany. These investigators developed the so-called vitalistic theory of fermentation. They proposed that if yeasts are introduced into a sugar-containing solution, they use the sugar as food and excrete the nonutilizable parts as alcohol and carbon dioxide. In the eyes of the chemists of that period, in particular von Liebig and Wöhler, this theory was completely unacceptable, and von Liebig countered with his mechanistic theory. His purely chemical fermentation theory left no room for the participation of a living substance. According to von Liebig, yeast is a substance which is continually in the process of chemical transformation. This was supposed to cause the decomposition of dissolved sugar into ethanol and CO_2 because the yeast was thought to impart its "atomic motion" to the sugar molecule. For many years von Liebig's views were generally accepted as the correct ones. It was the result of the genius of Pasteur, who, incidentally, was also trained as a chemist, that the vitalistic theory finally triumphed over the mechanistic theory. Pasteur, who had become more and more involved with biological problems, presented his views on fermentations in integrated form in his famous book, *Études sur la bière*, published in 1876. Pasteur postulated that the fermentation process for organisms living under anaerobic conditions (including both anaerobic bacteria and yeast) constituted a substitute for the respiratory process of aerobic organisms. In other words, the fermentation processes, such as alcoholic fermentation, are the vital energy-yielding processes of microorganisms living in the absence of oxygen: "La fermentation est la vie sans air."

Pasteur's demonstration that yeast also possesses respiratory ability and his experiments which tended to show that aeration repressed fermentation rounded out his studies on the physiological activities of yeast. This fundamental aspect of yeast metabolism, which was later studied in a more quantitative manner by Meyerhof, is now usually referred to as the "reaction of Pasteur-Meyerhof."

A partial return to the mechanistic theory occurred near the turn of the century as a result of the accidental discovery of the "zymase" of yeast in 1897 by Eduard Buchner. Many, including the great French investigator of yeasts, A. Guilliermond, considered this finding as the downfall of the fundamental part of Pasteur's fermentation theory. The Buchner brothers attempted to prepare an extract from brewer's yeast for medicinal purposes. They ground yeast with diatomaceous earth and squeezed out the juice in a mechanical press. They added sugar to the cell-free juice as a preservative and were startled to find that the juice began to bubble and froth. It was recognized that the process which took place was a cell-free alcoholic fermentation, and the agent responsible for the fermentation was termed zymase, now known to consist of a complex mixture of enzymes. In fact, the word "enzyme" is derived from the Greek, meaning "in yeast."

This discovery reduced the role of the yeast plant to the simple secretion of zymase, and many of the chemists of that period considered Bucher's discovery as the final victory of von Liebig's mechanistic theory. The "dead" zymase was now considered as a chemical or catalytic agent responsible for splitting sugar into alcohol and CO_2.

Subsequent investigations, however, have shown that the cell-free fermentation is quite unbalanced as compared to the process that takes place inside the living cell. The significance of fermentation to the living cell is the fact that fermentation (dissimilation) of sugar yields energy which enables the cell to utilize parts of the sugar molecule for growth (assimilation). These reactions, which occur in the living cytoplasm of the cell, have re-established the vitalistic theory of fermentation, which, with minor modifications, is the generally accepted one today.

Following the discovery of zymase many of the great biochemists of the twentieth century, including Neuberg, Meyerhof, Warburg, Wieland, Embden, Parnass, Harden, and others, contributed to the complete elucidation of the intermediary pathway and energetics of the fermentation process. The significance of their discoveries was greatly magnified when it was shown that these same reactions (often referred to as glycolysis) take place in many different types of living cells and that they represent a basic process by which an organism obtains, from sugar, energy for life.

After van Leeuwenhoek's initial description of yeast in 1680, very little additional information on its morphology was gained until the early nineteenth century. Starting about 1825, Cagniard de la Tour, Kützing, and Schwann, in their studies on beer and wine yeasts, showed that these organisms are cells which reproduce by budding. Much of this work was done by diluting a fermenting liquid until tiny droplets contained but one or at least very few cells, which enabled the microscopist to study reproduction of cells under a microscope. To prevent drying out during the period of observation, the droplets were placed on a coverslip of thin glass, which in turn was placed upside down on a glass slide with a hollowed-out area in the surface (a so-called moist-chamber), and the edges of the coverslip were sealed with wax or paraffin. Yeast cells in the droplets could then be observed during growth.

In 1839 Schwann observed intracellular bodies, "endospores," formed within yeast cells. He also noted the freeing of these internal bodies by rupture of the cell wall, but the significance of these spores was not at all understood.

De Bary, in 1866, compared the spore-containing bodies of yeast to the spore sac of ascospore-forming fungi termed *Ascomycetes*. Reess, in a series of experiments between 1868 and 1870, observed endospores in many species of yeasts, gave accurate descriptions of their shapes and their manner of germination by budding. He termed these endospores "ascospores" and the spore sac an "ascus" since he, too, noted the similarity in spore development with certain of the lower *Ascomycetes*. In 1870 he suggested the name *Saccharomyces* (previously used by Meyen in 1837, who first used the term for budding yeasts) for the spore-forming yeasts and included them in the *Ascomycetes*.

Later, in 1884, de Bary pointed out that yeast spores, as well as ascospores formed by the more complex *Ascomycetes*, are produced by "free cell formation," that is, the spore bodies are delimited within the protoplasm of the ascus, or spore sac, free from other spores and also free from attachment to the ascus wall. This is in contrast to the method of spore formation in other classes of fungi—notably the *Phycomycetes* and the *Basidiomycetes.*

Pasteur, among his many contributions to science, introduced methods for obtaining pure cultures, thus enabling more reliable morphological studies of yeasts. The great Danish student of yeast, Emil Christian Hansen, perfected these techniques and for thirty years he carefully studied morphological and certain physiological characteristics of yeasts. He was able to differentiate and characterize a large number of species, many of which are still recognized today. He attempted the first comprehensive system of yeast taxonomy in 1896. His career of meticulous investigations earned him recognition as the true founder of morphological studies of yeasts.

Hansen's recommendations of systematic relationships and life cycles of yeasts were greatly expanded by Guilliermond in Paris, who contributed much additional information on the physiology, sexuality, and phylogenetic relations of the yeasts in his monographs of 1920 and 1928. Guilliermond also devised various dichotomous keys for use in identifying yeast species.

Following Guilliermond, four monographs on the taxonomy of the major groups of yeasts emerged between 1931 and 1952 from the Technical University of Delft. These works, although not carrying his name, were largely inspired by the great Kluyver of the "Delft School." The first complete and usable scheme of classification for the sporulating yeasts was prepared by Stelling-Dekker in 1931. Subsequently, Lodder in 1934 and Diddens and Lodder in 1941 published two volumes on the non-sporeforming yeasts. The publication of these three studies brought some unity and order out of chaos in the field of yeast taxonomy and greatly facilitated the classification of yeast cultures by the average microbiologist. A more recent comprehensive classification of both the sporogenous and asporogenous yeasts was published in 1952 by Lodder and Kregervan Rij. This volume represents a careful examination and re-evaluation of 1317 strains of yeast maintained in the Yeast Division of the "Centraalbureau voor Schimmelcultures" housed in the Laboratory of Microbiology of the Technical University at Delft, Holland. At about the same time (1951) Wickerham in the United States introduced a number of novel techniques and principles in the classification of yeasts. For example, he introduced several synthetic media to study morphology, assimilation of a much more representative array of carbon compounds, and ability to grow with or without vitamins in such media (see Chapter VII). He also placed greater emphasis on the occurrence of yeasts in nature in the haploid or in the diploid form and on the existence of heterothallic mating types (see Chapters IV and V for further details).

A monograph comprising a somewhat different system of yeast taxonomy was published by the Russian taxonomist Kudriavzev in 1954. This is interesting because of some of his views on phylogeny of the ascospore-forming yeasts.

At the present time a number of taxonomists in various countries are cooperating in an expanded effort to bring the classification of the yeasts up to date. This is important because of the many new yeasts described during the last fifteen years and the vastly increased fundamental knowledge of this group of microfungi.

The historical developments sketched above have so far offered little information as to just what a yeast is. Early workers in the field, working with typical beer and wine yeasts, found these to be generally unicellular organisms reproducing by budding, and forming ascospores under suitable conditions within a mother cell or ascus. The origin of the word yeast relates primarily to its ability to ferment. Definitions applied to yeast according to their industrial behavior, such as "cultured, true, wild, top or bottom yeasts," have little meaning from a botanical point of view. They are confusing even from the industrial point of view, for a cultivated yeast considered desirable in a brewery may very well be considered a wild yeast in a bakery. Top-fermenting brewery yeasts generally rise to the surface of the liquid as a foam and should have the ability to split bond (a) and to ferment only the fructose portion of a trisaccharide raffinose (see below), leaving melibiose behind.

$$\underbrace{\text{Galactose } \alpha, 1 \rightarrow 6 \underbrace{\text{Glucose } \overbrace{\alpha, 1 \rightarrow 2, \beta \text{ Fructose}}^{\text{Sucrose}}}_{\text{(a)}}}_{\text{Melibiose}}$$

(b)

(raffinose molecule)

Bottom-brewing yeasts, on the other hand, should split both bonds (a) and (b) and ferment the entire raffinose molecule. In addition, the cells of a bottom yeast tend to settle to the bottom of the liquid soon after fermentation subsides. Though this differentiation is seemingly clearcut, such is not the case, for it leaves no room for forms that are intermediate in their sedimentation behavior, and these are known to exist.

From a botanical point of view, yeasts are indeed difficult to define as a single homogeneous group. A discussion of a "mushroom," or perhaps a "fern," would permit a listing of rather specific characteristics which all mushrooms or all ferns would have in common. Such specific characteristics are difficult to designate for the purpose of encompassing all yeasts. Botanists of the nineteenth century generally accepted the idea that yeasts belong to the plant kingdom. More specifically, yeasts belong to the division *Thallophyta*, whose members are broadly characterized as lacking true roots, stems, and leaves and as having rather simple reproductive structures. Size is not a criterion, for thallophytes range from single cells one micron (or one thousandth of a millimeter) in diameter, such as some bacteria, to giant sea kelps, 75 feet or more in length. All members of this group, however, are basically simple in structure and have relatively primitive mechanisms for re-production.

Yeasts lack chlorophyll and are unable to manufacture their organic needs by photosynthesis from inorganic components as do higher plants, algae, and even some bacteria. Therefore, they must live a saprophytic or parasitic life. Yeasts possess definite, rather rigid cell walls, have a well-organized nucleus, but lack any means of locomotion. These more restrictive properties fit only one of the ten subdivisions (phyla) of the *Thallophyta*, namely the *Eumycophyta*, or true fungi. Yeasts are usually defined as fungi which do not produce distinct aerial, asexual spores (conidia) and which spend at least part of the vegetative cycle as individual, single cells. Budding is not the only means of asexual reproduction by yeasts, since certain species reproduce vege-tatively by cross-wall formation (sometimes followed by fis-sion), and still others by a process intermediate between bud-ding and cross-wall formation. As is the case with most bio-logical materials, there are transitional forms between yeast and the more typical fungi, in which case the organisms in question are usually designated as yeast-like fungi. If we become more restrictive in our definition of the characteristics of various yeasts and yeast-like organisms than we use for the true fungi, we find that the yeasts, as a group, can no longer be placed in a single smaller subdivision or class. Actually, yeasts will be found in at least three of the four subgroupings (classes) established under the phylum of true fungi.

Yeasts best known to the average person are those used for producing beer, wine, and bread. These and numerous other yeasts share a common property with many higher fungi, namely the formation of spores by free-cell formation within a sac, the ascus. The ascus directly or indirectly originates as the result of sexual fusion between two specialized cells, or gametes. These properties characterize the class *Ascomycetes*.

Another group of yeasts does not form spores in an ascus but externally, on the tip of pointed, specialized structures called sterigmata. These spores are forcefully discharged (by a mechanism still not fully understood) and for this reason they are called ballistospores (see Chapter IV). The mechanism of producing these spores is characteristic of fungi classed as *Basidiomycetes*. Mushrooms, found in pasture and forest soils, bracket fungi growing on trees, as well as rusts and smuts which parasitize wheat and corn, are all members of this class.

Finally, there are yeasts which apparently are unable to form any type of sexual spores. These are placed in the class, *Fungi imperfecti (Deuteromycetes)*, with all other fungi whose sexual cycle is not known. Obviously, this is a heterogeneous collection in which artificial relationships are drawn as a result of asexual similarities.

To complicate the definition of yeast even more, some unicellular algae produce natural mutants devoid of chlorophyll. These colorless algae which are common in nature, and probably derived from *Chlorella*, are normally placed in the genus

Prototheca. They differ from the yeasts in that their vegetative reproduction involves neither budding nor fission but a kind of internal cell partitioning into an indefinite number of daughter cells. Nevertheless, they can be and have been mistaken for yeasts.

Mention might also be made of the fact that some fungi belonging to the class *Phycomycetes,* in particular some species of *Mucor,* grow entirely as mycelial molds on solid media. However, under more anaerobic conditions, particularly with carbon dioxide in the atmosphere, the fungus begins to multiply exactly like budding yeast cells.

This brief account of the historical development of the knowledge regarding yeast indicates that these organisms have been the objects of scientific attention for a long time. Nevertheless, it must be acknowledged that it is still difficult to define accurately what yeasts are and that as a group they form a heterogeneous association of organisms with scientifically fascinating properties.

II / Yeast Morphology

Yeast cells occurring in fermenting beverages, as first observed by van Leeuwenhoek and later studied by Cagniard de la Tour, Kützing and Schwann, were described as being round to oval in appearance and reproducing by forming buds which developed into daughter cells. The new cells separated from the mother cell and produced buds of their own. This description also fits the appearance of many other yeasts. Upon closer scrutiny, however, the shapes and methods of reproduction among the "yeasts" are quite varied.

Vegetative reproduction. With the exception of the development of the ascus, morphological properties are, in general, based on the characteristics of vegetative reproduction of a particular yeast (Fig. 1). Budding, as mentioned above, represents the

Fig. 1. Cell division by budding, cross-wall formation (septation), and bud-fission.

most common mode of reproduction. With the exception of a few genera, buds arise on the shoulders and at the ends of the long axes of vegetative cells. This type of budding is usually referred to as "multilateral" and is characteristic of *Saccharomyces* and most other genera. In the case of spherical cells (often found in species of *Debaryomyces*), where no axes are apparent, buds arise any place on the surface of the cell. In contrast to the multilaterally budding yeasts, there are several genera (*e.g.* *Hanseniaspora* and *Kloeckera*) where budding is restricted to the tips of the cell (polar budding). Such yeasts are known as apiculate or lemon-shaped yeasts; the shape results from the budding process. In one genus, *Trigonopsis*, which characteristically has triangularly shaped cells, budding is restricted to the three corners of such cells.

Two genera, *Endomyces* and *Schizosaccharomyces* (Fig. 2a), reproduce vegetatively exclusively by fission. In this case, reproduction is carried out by the formation of septa, or cross-walls, without any constriction of the original cell wall. When the process is complete the cross-wall divides into two individual walls and the newly formed cells can then separate.

In a few instances a type of vegetative reproduction occurs which is intermediate between budding and cross-wall formation. This so-called "bud-fission" results from a type of budding in which we find a very broad neck at the base of the bud, somewhat like a bowling pin. Subsequent formation of a septum across the isthmus separates the bud from the mother cell. Examples of this type of reproduction may be found in *Saccharomycodes* (2b), *Nadsonia,* and in *Pityrosporum*. It should be pointed out that this type of reproduction is not fundamentally different from that occurring in a typical budding yeast. It is largely a difference in size of the cross-wall formed, which in the case of budding yeasts, as *Saccharomyces* (2c), is so small that it gives the impression under the light microscope that the bud is "pinched off" (see also Chapter III).

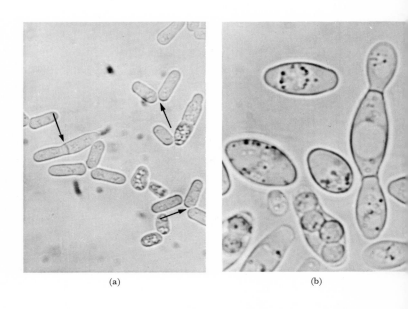

(a)   (b)

Fig. 2. Vegetative reproduction of yeast: (a) cells reproducing by cross-wall formation (*Schizosaccharomyces*); (b) bipolar budding and separation of buds by cross-wall formation;

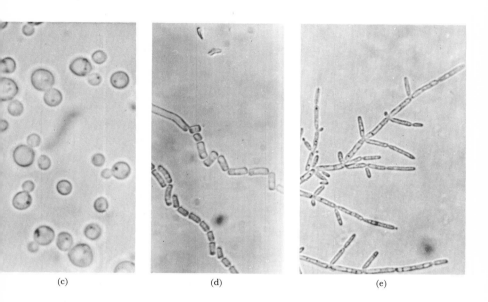

(c)   (d)   (e)

"bud-fission" (*Saccharomycodes*); (c) budding cells (*Saccharomyces*);
(d) mycelial hyphae breaking up into arthrospores (*Trichosporon*);
(e) pseudomycelium formation (*Candida*).

Yeasts are also known which utilize both budding and fission as means for vegetative reproduction. Members of the genus *Trichosporon* (2d) usually grow in the form of hyphal strands, containing cross-walls at regular intervals. These strands can undergo disarticulation, or breaking up along the cross-walls into individual cells called arthrospores (or "oidia" by some). On a solid medium, arthrospores are often seen in a zig-zag formation somewhat resembling the position assumed by cars of a derailed railroad train. In addition, a variable number of budding cells can arise on the mycelial strands. In *Endomycopsis,* and in certain species of *Candida*, hyphae with cross-walls and bud formation are found, but in these two genera the hyphae generally do not break up into arthrospores.

The thallus. The thallus, or soma, is the vegetative body or structure of a yeast. The manner in which the component cells of such a structure are arranged may be very characteristic for certain species or genera.

In its simplest form the thallus may be a single cell or perhaps one with its daughter cell still attached, as is the case in *Saccharomyces cerevisiae*. In this instance the first bud usually detaches as soon as the mother cell produces a second bud. In other yeasts, however, buds may remain attached to the mother cell and the first daughter cell, as well as the mother cell, can produce additional buds and so on. This may result in small to large clusters or chains of cells.

Chain formation can lead to a structure called a pseudomycelium (false mycelium). A pseudomycelium (Fig. 2e) arises when, instead of the bud breaking away from the mother cell upon maturity, it stays attached, elongates, and continues to bud in turn. Often the area where two cells join widens, giving the impression of a true cross-wall. In this manner, strands are formed which in appearance resemble true mycelium (cells separated by a cross-wall), differing only in the manner in which the new cells arise (budding).

Development of pseudomycelia ranges from the very primitive, in which the number of cells is limited and where there is little or no differentiation between the cells, to those in which there is marked differentiation between the cells comprising the main stem (usually composed of rather elongated cells) and the buds arising in clusters on the shoulders of these elongated cells (Fig. 3). These side buds may remain spherical to

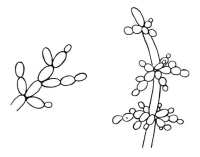

Fig. 3. At right, a characteristic branch of a well-developed pseudomycelium; left, a primitive pseudomycelium.

oval or they may elongate themselves, giving rise to further branching. As a means of differentiating the spherical or oval buds from the pseudomycelial or stem cells the former are termed blastospores. The French term "appareil sporifere" is also used by some authors. While a given species may produce a characteristic form of pseudomycelium, very often several types of pseudomycelia may be found within the same species. Thus while the ability or inability to form pseudomycelia has value in characterizing a yeast, the type of pseudomycelium is of lesser value. A few examples of pseudomycelia are illustrated in Figs. 2e and 3.

Cell morphology. Besides spherical, globose, ovoid, elongated, and cylindrical vegetative cells, which may arise as a result of the modes of vegetative reproduction discussed above, there are certain yeasts with highly characteristic cell shapes (Fig. 4). The lemon-shaped or apiculate vegetative cell is characteristic of a group of yeasts commonly found in the early stages of natural fermentation of fruits and other sugary materials (*Hanseniaspora* and *Kloeckera*). An ogival cell shape is one in which an elongated cell is rounded at one extremity and somewhat pointed at the other. This shape is characteristic of yeasts called *Brettanomyces*, which have been used for many years in the production of ale in Ireland, Great Britain, and Belgium. The so-called "bottle bacillus," associated with dandruff, is a yeast with a flask-like cell shape. This yeast (*Pityrosporum*) reproduces vegetatively by bud-fission, thus giving rise to a bottle- or flask-shape. The triangular cells of *Trigonopsis* are unique. The single species of this genus was isolated from beer in a Munich brewery.

To say that a particular shape is characteristic of a given species or genus does not mean that every cell in a population will be of that shape. However, at some period in the onto-

Fig. 4. Various cell shapes and modes of reproduction. From left to right: spheroidal, ovoidal, cylindroidal, ogival, triangular, flask-shaped, apiculate.

genetic development of each cell it will appear in that form. Ontogeny is the term referring to the history or development of an individual organism. For example, the apiculate (lemon-shaped) yeasts generally start as spherical to oval buds which separate from the mother cell and in turn develop buds them-

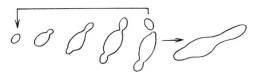

Fig. 5. Development of characteristic cell shapes in an apiculate yeast (*Hanseniaspora*). This is an example of ontogeny—the development of an individual.

selves (Fig. 5). Since budding is bipolar, a young oval cell developing buds at its extremities then becomes lemon-shaped in appearance. Older cells, because of repeated bipolar budding, may assume a variety of shapes, although in old age an irregular elongated shape is common.

Some yeast cells may be 2–3 microns in length whereas other cells may attain lengths of 20–50 microns. The width is less variable and usually ranges between 1 and 10 microns. The actual size of the vegetative cells in a young culture may be quite uniform in some species or extremely heterogeneous in size and shape in others. This disparity may be used to differentiate between species or, in some instances, between varieties of the same species. Observation of the size and shape of vegetative cells as well as the manner in which they reproduce vegetatively is observed both in liquid media and on solid media. Very frequently malt extract is used, although synthetic media have been recommended for this purpose, since these are more reproducible in their composition. While a certain amount of variation is normal and to be expected within a yeast culture, age, environment, and cultural conditions can exert a profound influence on the culture's morphological properties. For this reason, descriptions of the various yeast species are based on results obtained under fairly standardized conditions.

III / Cytology

In discussing the cytology and cellular organization of yeasts, one must be aware of significant differences between various species. Most of our information on cytology is based on work with *Saccharomyces cerevisiae*, or baker's yeast. In more recent years, however, investigators have become interested in species belonging to different genera in order to bring out particular facets which are much more striking in some yeasts than in others. Furthermore, it should be pointed out that cytological changes may be brought about in a very striking way by the cultural conditions under which a yeast is grown prior to study. For example, the thickness of the wall, shape of the cell, lipid content, presence of vacuoles and inclusion bodies, and the presence or absence of capsules can be strongly modified by the growing conditions (Figs. 6a, b, c).

Information on the cytology of yeast has been gathered by (i) direct observation with the light microscope; (ii) after staining with specific dyes, particularly to determine the localization of certain components; (iii) electron microscopy of isolated cell walls; and (iv) electron microscopy of ultra-thin sections of a yeast cell. We shall review the results of these various approaches while discussing the principal cell components.

The micro-structures of a yeast cell are the following: The cell wall, cytoplasmic membrane, nucleus, one or more vac-

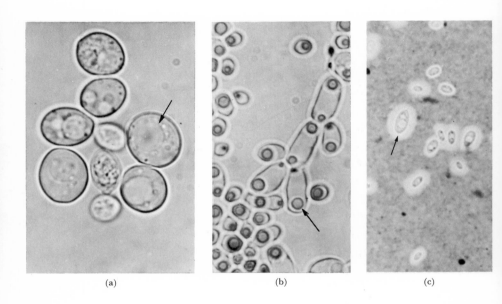

(a)   (b)   (c)

Fig. 6. Structures of yeast cells: (a) vacuoles (*Saccharomyces*); (b) lipid (oil) globules (*Hansenula*); (c) capsules photographed against a background of India ink. The India ink particles do not penetrate the capsular material, resulting in light halos (*Cryptococcus*).

uoles, mitochondria, lipid globules, volutin or polyphosphate bodies, and the cytoplasmic matrix.

We shall discuss below in more detail specific information known about these individual components and, in particular, point out how information on the nature, the chemical composition, and the appearance of these components has been obtained.

The cell wall. The wall can be seen with the ordinary light microscope as a distinct outline of the cell and although it is somewhat elastic, its rigidity is responsible for the particular shape which a yeast cell assumes. Under the light microscope, even with the highest magnification possible, the cell wall does not reveal distinct features and appears as a fairly smooth outline of the cell sometimes dotted with slight irregularities.

Much more information on the physical appearance of yeast cell walls has been obtained as a result of the advent of electron microscopy and the possibility of preparing isolated walls. Whole yeast cells are too electron-dense to permit seeing any details of the wall structure, but cells which have been broken in a sonic oscillator, or by other means, can be washed free of cytoplasmic contents and studied effectively with the electron microscope. Such studies are facilitated when the walls are boiled in dilute NaOH or HCl, because the cell wall itself is relatively electron-dense. When boiled in dilute HCl the smooth-appearing walls change strikingly into a fibrillar mat, somewhat resembling a piece of felt cloth under high magnification. Presumably the wall consists of several layers, but these are not usually distinct in electron micrographs.

The most conspicuous features of the smooth-appearing walls are (i) a birth scar and (ii) a number of bud scars. A birth scar is a structure resulting from the formation of the cell from its mother cell by the budding process. Birth scars normally occur at one end of the long axis of the cell and do not have a highly characteristic appearance. Upon alkali treatment this scar assumes a more granular appearance than does the rest of the wall. Bud scars are formed when the new cell in turn produces daughter cells by budding. Bud scars, when viewed from the outside of the wall, show a circular brim, slightly raised above the cell surface. The brim surrounds a slightly sunken area, which shows a concentric pattern around a small central depression. The number of bud scars depends on how many daughter cells a yeast cell has produced.

Investigators have followed the number of buds which cells of strains of *Saccharomyces cerevisiae* can produce and found a range of 9–43 buds per cell with a median of 24. In most of the common yeasts, such as those belonging to *Saccharomyces*, successive buds are never formed at the same place on the wall; instead, they originate usually on opposite polar regions of the yeast cell. Thus, bud scars are found in greatest numbers toward the ends of the long axes of ovoid cells. After the production of three or four daughter cells the mother cell gradually assumes a different appearance, and surface irregularities can sometimes be seen, even with the light microscope. Under ideal conditions a yeast cell may duplicate in a time period between one and two hours, but after many buds have been produced the generation time lengthens and finally may become as long as six hours. Finally the cell dies. Only in the case of yeasts with lemon-shaped or apiculate cells, where budding occurs exclusively at the two poles, are the bud scars superimposed on each other, giving a peculiar type of scar tissue, characterized by collar-like, concentric rings.

Naturally, bud scars are not found in fission yeasts. It can be shown in longitudinal sections of *Schizosaccharomyces* cells that cross-wall formation occurs by an annular centripetal growth of an inner lateral portion of the cell wall, without the formation of a cell plate. This results ultimately in the complete development of a transverse cell wall, dividing the original cell into two new ones.

Our present understanding of the chemical composition of the cell wall of yeast is based largely on the combined evidence of chemical analysis and enzymatic degradation of the walls. Data have become much more meaningful since clean, purified cell walls, free of cytoplasmic inclusions, became available. Again, most of the work has been done with species of *Saccharomyces*, although more recently other yeasts also have been investigated. We shall first confine ourselves to the composition of *Saccharomyces* walls and then contrast this information with what is known about other yeasts.

The principal fraction, now known as yeast glucan, and in the early literature as "yeast cellulose," constitutes the component responsible for the shape and rigidity of the yeast cell. This highly insoluble polysaccharide has been shown to contain a preponderance of β-1,3 linkages between the glucose units which compose this polymer. True cellulose of higher plants has β-1,4 bonds. The presence of β-1,6 linkages has also been demonstrated in yeast glucan. Most of the evidence points to a branched structure for this polysaccharide. Some yeasts appear to contain glucans with different proportions of β-1,3 and β-1,6 bonds. In addition, evidence for other bonds between the glucose units has been obtained by the use of bacterial enzymes which have defined β-1,3 and β-1,6 glucanase activity.

While these enzymes can attack walls of *Saccharomyces cerevisiae*, they are very limited in their activity on the walls of certain other yeasts.

The glucan, which represents about 30–35% of the dried cell walls of *S. cerevisiae*, is accompanied by a second major component, a mannan, consisting of a water-soluble polysaccharide of the sugar D-mannose. This polymer is also present in a concentration of approximately 30%. Mannan can be extracted from yeast cell walls by dilute alkali and can be precipitated as its copper salt by treating the extract with cold Fehling solution. The precipitate dissolves in dilute acid and can be reprecipitated with alcohol. In this way the mannan can be readily purified. Chemical analysis indicates that mannan is a strongly branched polysaccharide of high molecular weight, containing α-1,6, α-1,2, and, to a lesser extent, α-1,3 linkages between the mannose residues. There are also yeasts which do not contain this type of mannan in their walls. This applies to the species of *Nadsonia, Schizosaccharomyces, Rhodotorula, Sporobolomyces,* and mycelial yeast-like organisms belonging to *Endomyces* and *Eremascus*.

Yeast mannan is usually associated with protein components. Some workers believe that the mannan and the protein are chemically linked together and that this association is broken only after fairly drastic treatment of the yeast cell walls with alkali. The protein content of cell-wall preparations depends on the degree of purification. Since some investigators have more carefully removed cytoplasmic inclusions than others, figures for protein content vary considerably. However, a value of approximately 6–8% protein is generally accepted as indicative of the protein content of baker's yeast walls. It is very likely that at least some of this protein represents enzymes involved in the uptake and breakdown of substrates which cannot enter the cells until they are partially degraded.

Another component is chitin, a linear polymer of N-acetylglucosamine, in which the constituent monomeric units are linked by β-1,4 bonds. Chitin is best known in the exo-skeleton of insects and in the shell of crustacea, but, since chitin from yeast is more easily solubilized than that of the above-mentioned animals, it is believed to occur in a somewhat less highly polymerized form. On the other hand, X-ray patterns of yeast chitin are similar to those of crustacean chitin.

Chitin concentrations of 1–2% are found in walls of *S. cerevisiae* and related species. In the filamentous yeasts (e.g. *Endomyces*) and in the genera *Nadsonia, Rhodotorula,* and *Sporobolomyces* the chitin content is much higher. In contrast to this, chitin is lacking in the three recognized species of *Schizosaccharomyces* (the fission yeasts).

Yeasts which lack chitin or mannan contain glucan components with properties different from those found in *Saccharomyces cerevisiae.* Besides showing a variation in resistance to enzymatic degradation, these glucans have a much greater solubility in alkali. The glucan of baker's yeast is virtually insoluble in alkali, but the glucans of several other yeasts (for example, those of *Rhodotorula,* the red yeasts) are essentially soluble in alkali.

Wall material of baker's yeast has been reported by some to contain from 8.5–13.5% lipid material, although lower figures have been published by others. There is no question, though, that lipid constitutes an important structural material of the wall of yeast cells.

Finally, cell-wall material is known to contain from one to several percent of inorganic materials, especially phosphate.

Capsular materials. In discussing the cell walls of yeast, mention must also be made of the presence of capsular materials (Fig. 6c) and other extracellular substances formed by yeasts. The principal categories in this connection are phosphomannans, starch-like substances, heteropolysaccharides (containing more than one type of sugar unit), and finally hydrophobic substances belonging to the sphingolipid type of compounds. A brief discussion of these various materials will be given.

Primitive species of *Hansenula* (species which are usually associated with bark beetles that attack coniferous trees) and those of closely related genera (*Pichia* and *Pachysolen*) produce extracellular phosphomannans. These slimy, viscous polymers are water-soluble and form a sticky layer on the surface of the cells. They contain only the sugar D-mannose and phosphate, the latter linked as a diester. The molar ratio of mannose to phosphate is characteristic of the species producing the phosphomannan.

Species of *Cryptococcus*, *Lipomyces*, and certain others produce different kinds of slimy capsular polysaccharides. Relatively little is known about the composition of these capsular materials. There is evidence, however, that they do contain hexose sugars, pentose sugars, and in some cases possibly uronic acids, such as glucuronic acid (heteropolysaccharides). In *Rhodotorula* a novel exocellular mannan, with alternately linked β-1,3 and β-1,4 mannopyranose residues arranged in a straight chain, has been discovered recently.

In addition, species of *Cryptococcus* are characterized by the production, in acidic media, of iodophilic substances which stain either deep blue or purplish with iodine. Some members of this genus excrete these substances into the medium, and in others the "starch" remains associated with the cells. The formation of starch-like compounds is not limited entirely to species of *Cryptococcus*, since these substances have also been observed in a few species belonging to *Candida, Trichosporon,* and *Rhodotorula.*

Several of the so-called advanced, film-forming species of *Hansenula*, in particular *H. ciferrii*, form on their surface tetra-acetylphytosphingosine and triacetyl dihydrosphingosine. These are complex hydrophobic compounds which appear to be responsible, at least in part, for the tendency of these yeasts to form pellicles in liquid media and for the mat appearance of their colonies (see Chapter VI).

The cytoplasmic membrane. This structure is located directly beneath the cell wall and plays an important role in the selective permeability of the cell and in the transport of nutrients. The cytoplasmic membrane is not a smooth layer, but short invaginations into the cytoplasm are apparent when ultra-thin sections of *S. cerevisiae* are photographed with the electron microscope. The membrane is very thin, about 75 to 80 Å, and appears as a double layer in electron micrographs. It is composed of protein, ribonucleic acid, and lipids.

The existence of a cytoplasmic membrane can be demonstrated very nicely by treating yeast cells with the digestive fluid of snails, which has the property of dissolving the outer cell wall. If this process is carried out in the presence of an osmotic buffer (for example, in the presence of 0.8 molar D-mannitol or other nonutilizable sugar) the cell wall is dissolved and the cell, irrespective of its original morphology, assumes a spherical shape (a spheroplast) held together by the very thin cytoplasmic membrane. If the osmotic pressure of the suspending fluid is lowered by diluting with water, for example, the spheroplast swells and the cytoplasmic membrane readily bursts releasing the cell contents to the medium.

The nucleus. Although in the past many controversies raged about the location and the nature of the yeast nucleus, it is now well established, as a result of studying ultra-thin sections, that yeast has a well-defined nucleus, surrounded by a double nuclear membrane. This membrane contains a number of nuclear pores, presumably for the purpose of exchanging cytoplasmic materials with nuclear components. All of the earlier work was based on staining the nucleus with specific dyes, but in most cases the details of nuclear division could not be clearly observed. The demonstration of individual chromosomes was even more difficult, although some workers demonstrated by use of nuclear stains individual bodies which resembled chromosomes.

A great deal of detailed information relating to nuclear behavior has been obtained by use of ultra-thin sections of yeast. This work has shown that during budding the yeast nucleus divides by a constriction process. Initially, the chromatin material apparently divides within the nuclear membrane which remains intact. The nuclear membrane then constricts, dividing the nucleus into two separate entities, one of which migrates into the daugther cell. That the nuclear membrane remains intact in yeast is a highly unusual characteristic, differing greatly from that of most higher organisms. Because of the electron transparency of the nucleus, internal structures cannot be observed easily with the electron microscope; hence, but slight evidence for the presence of individual chromosomes has thus far been obtained. Present information about individual chromosomes is based on genetic evidence and by use of specific staining techniques. Typical spindle formation has never been observed, and migration of chromosomes appears to be quite different from the process in higher plants. By use of serial thin sections through the nuclei of certain yeasts it has been possible to observe structures with a higher electron density than that occurring in the rest of the nucleus. It is believed that this dense material is the nucleolus of yeast.

Vacuoles. Usually one or more vacuoles of variable size can be readily observed in yeast cells under the light microscope (Fig. 6a). Vacuoles are probably sacs of fluid of greater transparency and lower viscosity than the surrounding cytoplasm. Classical studies by Guilliermond have shown that certain dyes (such as neutral red) can penetrate living cells, without causing damage, and accumulate in the vacuoles giving them a pink appearance in contrast to a colorless cytoplasm. This can be demonstrated particularly well by using the yeast-like organism *Geotrichum candidum.*

More recently, other workers have found that if yeasts are grown in the presence of L-methionine, the vacuole accumulates large amounts of S-adenosylmethionine, a substance which strongly absorbs ultraviolet light at 265 mμ. This causes the vacuoles to look black in photomicrographs taken with ultraviolet light. S-adenosylmethionine, which is very slowly metabolized by *Candida utilis* (a yeast particularly suitable for these studies), is passed on to the vacuoles of daughter cells for several generations, when the cells are subsequently cultured in media not containing L-methionine.

Occasionally the vacuoles contain very striking "dancing bodies" (due to Brownian movement), which consist of highly refractile polymetaphosphate or volutin.

Vacuoles are less electron-dense than the cytoplasm, so that they can be easily differentiated in electron micrographs. They are surrounded by single membranes, which appear to have diverticula, or finger-like structures, that extend deep into the cytoplasm.

Mitochondria. Yeast cells have been shown by ultra-thin sectioning to contain mitochondria (varying in number from about four to twenty), which, in *Saccharomyces cerevisiae*, are located fairly close to the periphery of the yeast cell. In *Rhodotorula glutinis*, however, they are more randomly distributed throughout the cytoplasm. These bodies, also found in cells of higher plants and animals, measure approximately 0.4–0.6 micron in lengths and 0.2–0.3 micron in diameter, and are important in the respiratory activity of yeast. Yeast mitochondria have a double-layered outer wall and contain internal membranes, or cristae, in various configurations. These cristae, which are characteristic components of mitochondria, appear to be formed by infolding of the inner layer of the membrane.

Lipid globules. Most yeast cells contain small amounts of lipid in the form of globules which are stainable with fat stains such as Sudan Black or Sudan Red. These dyes penetrate the cell and accumulate in the lipid globules, staining them bluish black or red. In electron micrographs of thin sections, the lipid globules show up as the most electron-transparent bodies of the cell. Some species, as *Rhodotorula glutinis,* contain rather numerous lipid globules of various sizes. Other yeasts (*e.g. Lipomyces starkeyi* and *Candida pulcherrima*) frequently have one or two very large fat globules (Fig. 6b). Baker's yeast and other species of *Saccharomyces,* however, have a relatively low fat content.

Cytoplasm. Cytoplasm is a limpid fluid encompassing finely granular material which contains the reserve polysaccharide yeast glycogen, and is rich in ribonucleic acid and protein.

The last two are found primarily in small RNA-containing granules, called ribosomes, which appear to be involved in protein synthesis. Yeast ribosomes have been studied in the analytical ultracentrifuge and electron microscope, and five size-classes (from 30S to 120S) have been distinguished. The proportions vary in relative abundance with the physiological state of the cell. The glycogen content varies considerably and may be demonstrated in yeast colonies by treating them with iodine. Cells which are high in glycogen content turn deep brown in color by this treatment.

Several investigators have reported on the basis of serial thin sections that the cytoplasm contains an extensive membrane system. The function of this membrane system is not known. Whether or not these internal membranes are similar to the endoplasmic reticulum known to exist in cells of higher organisms is a matter of speculation.

IV / Sporulation and Life Cycles

In mycology the designation "spore" is a rather general term, indicating a reproductive cell. Both asexual and sexual spores are formed by yeasts. Examples of asexual spores, which are actually no more than unicellular structures produced by a larger vegetative body, or thallus, are blastospores (simple budding cells), arthrospores (which are single-celled fission products of mycelial hyphae) and chlamydospores (which are rather thick-walled resting spores produced by certain yeasts).

Another type of spore is the so-called ballistospore which is produced by members of the family *Sporobolomycetaceae*. These spores are borne, one at a time, on pointed stalks (sterigmata), and they are discharged from these stalks with considerable force by a peculiar droplet mechanism. It has been demonstrated that a small droplet is exuded by the stalk at the base of the spore, and that actually the droplet is discharged, carrying the spore with it (Fig. 7). Because of the similarity of this process with the mechanism of spore formation and discharge in the *Basidiomycetes* (to which the mushrooms and bracket fungi belong), it is fairly generally assumed that the yeasts belonging to this group are primitive forms of the *Basidiomycetes*. Some cytological evidence supports this contention, but more work is needed to firmly establish their taxonomic position. Ballistospores are either asymmetric in shape (often kidney-shaped) as in the genus *Sporobolomyces* or symmetrical (generally ovoid) as in the genus *Bullera*.

Most of this chapter will deal with the formation of ascospores in yeasts, about which much more is known. The formation of ascospores is of great biological significance. Because sporulation constitutes a phase of the sexual life cycle of a yeast, that is, alternation of the haploid condition (1 n chromosomes) and the diplophase (2 n chromosomes), this cycle enables a yeast to exploit more fully the evolutionary processes, such as mutation, hybridization, and selection, which are so well known in the higher forms of life.

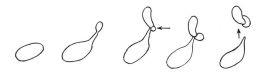

Fig. 7. Formation and discharge of a ballistospore by a species of *Sporobolomyces*.

Let us now consider the sporulation process in greater detail. A basic aspect of sporulation is the reduction division, or meiosis, which a diploid nucleus undergoes. Although the behavior of chromosomes during meiosis is extremely variable in different organisms, the principle of the process is basically similar in both plants (to which the yeasts belong) and animals. The nucleus of a diploid yeast cell (e.g. *Saccharomyces cerevisiae*) arises through the fusion of the nuclei of two haploid cells, or of two spores, and thus contains the 2 n number of chromosomes. In meiosis the diploid chromosome complement is reduced again to the haploid number. A diploid chromosome complement consists of a number of pairs (represented by n) of chromosomes. Although yeast chromosomes are too small to be seen under a microscope, it is assumed, on the basis of analogy with higher forms of life, that the two members of each pair have a similar appearance. The two members of each pair are called homologous chromosomes and they are derived from each of the originally haploid cells which fused. During meiosis the homologous chromosomes approach each other and become tightly paired. Each chromosome of a pair splits lengthwise into two halves (chromatids), thus forming a four-strand structure, or tetrad. The tetrads, which meanwhile become shorter and more compact, then break apart into two dyads which separate during the first meiotic division. Next, the dyads divide into individual chromosomes (by division of their centromere), and their separation constitutes the second meiotic division. Thus, the two meiotic divisions result in the formation of four haploid nuclei, each carrying one chromatid of the original tetrad. It should be mentioned here that the haploid nuclei formed in this way are not necessarily identical to those of the two cells which gave rise to the original diploid cell. The reason for this is that during the formation of the above-mentioned four-stranded structure, or tetrad, breakage of chromatids may occur and this is followed by an exchange of parts of the chromatids and rejoining of the broken parts. This interchange of parts between homologous chromosomes, which has been termed crossing-over, has been demonstrated in yeast by genetic experiments.

Depending on the yeast, the four nuclei resulting from meiosis may undergo one additional duplication as in the case of *Schizosaccharomyces octosporus*, a species which characteristically forms eight spores in each ascus. Occasionally, further divisions of some or all of the haploid nuclei results in more numerous nuclei in each cell undergoing meiosis. The latter is characteristic of species of the genus *Kluyveromyces*. Cytoplasm then distributes itself around the various nuclei, a spore wall begins to become visible, and finally the spores become sharply delineated in their characteristic shape. This process is called sporulation by free-cell formation, in contrast to spore formation by the appearance of cleavage planes through the cytoplasm of the cell (partitioning) characteristic of certain other fungi.

Some of the cytoplasm remains free of the spores and is referred to as epiplasm. In some yeasts, after sporulation is complete, the ascus wall (the former cell wall) is rapidly digested by intracellular enzymes and the spores are liberated. In other yeasts the ascus wall remains intact and the spores are liberated only after they swell and rupture the ascus by force. At any rate, the spores, upon germination, can re-establish the diploid condition in a variety of ways, and the cycle can then start over again. It might be well to stress at this point that many yeasts require special growing conditions to pass through the sexual cycle. If these conditions are not met, a yeast may continue to propagate virtually indefinitely in the vegetative form.

Life cycles. The yeasts which live in various natural habitats can be placed into two broad groups, diploid and haploid. In a diploid yeast (such as *Saccharomyces cerevisiae*) reduction division can occur under suitable conditions directly from the vegetative cells as briefly described above. In haploid cells (for example, all of the species of *Schizosaccharomyces*) the nucleus of the vegetative cell contains the basic, or 1 n, number of chromosomes, so two such nuclei must first be transformed into a diploid nucleus before sporulation can take place. This happens in a variety of ways that will be illustrated later.

In the case of diploid yeasts, which produce ascospores directly in the vegetative cells, four mechanisms are known by which the diploid condition is re-established in the vegetative phase, thus completing the life cycle. These mechanisms (see Fig. 8) are as follows:

1. Two ascospores may fuse directly in the ascus. This results in nuclear fusion (karyogamy) of the two haploid nuclei, and the first vegetative cell resulting from this zygote (conjugated spores) is a diploid cell. This process occurs in *Saccharomycodes ludwigii*.

2. The ascospores may germinate into relatively small haploid vegetative cells. After a limited number of generations, fusion occurs between two of these cells, resulting in a diploid generation comprised of cells of somewhat larger dimensions than the initial haploid cells. This takes place in some strains of *Saccharomyces cerevisiae*.

3. A variation of the second mode occurs when only one or two of the spores produce a number of small haploid cells; one of these haploid cells fuses with another as yet ungerminated spore of the ascus, again resulting in the diploid generation. This also is found in certain strains of *S. cerevisiae*.

4. The last mechanism of diploidization consists in the division of the haploid nucleus inside the swelling ascospore, resulting in two haploid nuclei, which then fuse together in the germinating ascospore, producing a diploid nucleus. The first bud, then, resulting from the germinating ascospore, already constitutes a diploid cell. This mode of action is limited to homothallic yeasts (those in which sex differentiation is absent). This mechanism occurs in *Saccharomyces chevalieri* and in species of *Hanseniaspora*.

The life cycle of yeasts which characteristically spend their vegetative life in the haploid condition is quite different. In yeasts of this type the diploid generation is usually of very short

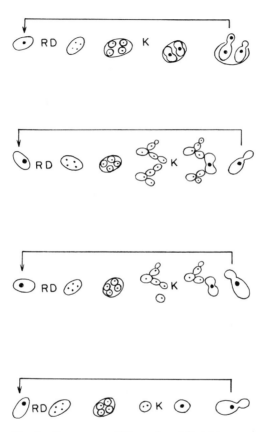

Fig. 8. Four types of life cycles of diploid yeasts (see text for details). Heavy dots represent diploid nuclei and light dots are haploid nuclei. K = karyogamy; RD = reduction division.

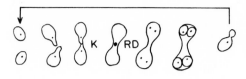

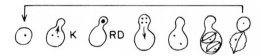

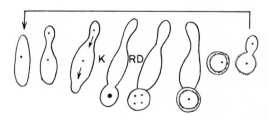

Fig. 9.   Three types of life cycles of haploid
yeasts (see text for details). Heavy dots represent
diploid nuclei and light dots are haploid nuclei.
K = karyogamy; RD = reduction division.

duration, existing only as a zygote after the fusion of two haploid cells and their nuclei. The life cycle of haploid yeasts takes place by the following mechanisms (see Fig. 9).

1. The vegetative cells form tube-like outgrowths which are called conjugation tubes. The tips of two conjugation tubes then grow together and a fusion canal is established through which the nuclei of the two cells can approach each other. They then undergo karyogamy resulting in a diploid nucleus. In the great majority of cases meiosis, or reduction division, immediately follows the conjugation process and the nuclei produce ascospores in a dumbbell-shaped ascus (the original zygote). If the two conjugating partners (gametes) appear morphologically identical we term the process isogamic conjugation. If there are four spores they may be divided two and two in the two halves of the dumbbell-shaped zygote, or they may occur as three in one half and one in the other half, and occasionally even as four and zero (Fig. 10). This depends on where the diploid nucleus undergoes reduction division and on the movement of the haploid nuclei thus formed. Examples are *Schizosaccharomyces pombe* and *Saccharomyces elegans.*

2. The second type of life cycle of the haploid yeasts occurs as follows. The haploid cell produces a bud, but the bud does not separate from the mother cell and retains a connective opening of rather large diameter. Nuclear division occurs (mitosis), and the two nuclei then move toward the bud in which karyogamy occurs. Meiosis then follows and two or four haploid nuclei are produced. Because this process occurs in a bud-like structure, the latter has been termed the "meiosis bud." The nuclei then move back to the mother cell and ascospore formation takes place. In yeasts following this type of life cycle, usually only one or two spores are formed and the extra nuclei,

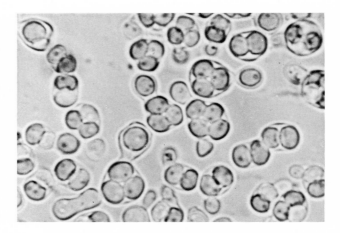

Fig. 10. Asci and ascospores of a haploid species of *Saccharomyces* (note dumbbell-shaped asci and spore distribution).

if present, presumably either degenerate or become incorporated in the ascospores. This type of life cycle has been demonstrated in the genus *Schwanniomyces* (Fig. 9, middle), but, by
morphological analogy, it may be presumed to occur also in
some species of *Hansenula, Pichia,* and in those species of
Saccharomyces formerly placed in the genus *Torulaspora.*

3. Another type of life cycle also involves the fusion of two
"gametes," but the dikaryotic cell thus formed does not become
the ascus. Instead, the nuclei (usually in close association with
each other) now move to a specialized cell, which originates
from the dikaryotic structure and is to become the ascus. In
the young ascus the nuclei undergo fusion, followed by reduction division and ascospore formation (Fig. 9, bottom). In this
type of life cycle the gametes may be of different size and shape
(*Nadsonia* and *Endomyces*), in which case we speak of heterogamic
conjugation. Where the gametes are similar in size and shape
the process is referred to as isogamic conjugation (*Endomycopsis*
and *Eremascus*).

The reader should be aware that the strict separation of yeasts
into haploid and diploid vegetative types is not possible. There
are certain yeasts in which (at least in laboratory cultures)
haploid and diploid cells may occur side by side. Hence, in a
sporulating culture we may find some asci which are the result
of conjugation between two cells and others that arose from
diploid cells. Wickerham, on the basis of his extensive studies
on the genus *Hansenula,* has expressed the view that the most
primitive species are haploid (those usually associated with
coniferous trees) and the most advanced (or free-living) species
are exclusively diploid. In between we find species (often isolated from broadleaf trees) in which various ratios of haploid to
diploid cells occur. Diploid cells can arise in a haploid culture

by zygote formation. The zygote may bud for a number of generations as diploid cells before sporulation finally takes place.

One of the first tests used in identifying a yeast, after it has been obtained in pure culture, is its ability to form ascospores. As pointed out above, however, the life cycle of a yeast does not consist of a rhythmic alternation of generations. Some yeasts will continue to grow vegetatively for many generations, and only under very special conditions can the sexual cycle be induced to occur. In the following section, therefore, the questions, "How does a yeast sporulate?" and "What induces a yeast to form ascospores?" will be considered.

Induction of sporulation. At one time it was a common belief that a yeast would sporulate only under conditions unfavorable for growth. Today, however, it is generally accepted that sporulation in yeast is not necessarily the result of exposure of the culture to unfavorable conditions. This is evident from the fact that isolates of many yeasts, which have recently been obtained from natural sources, often sporulate heavily upon rich nutrient media such as malt agar, yeast autolysate-glucose agar, and other commonly used isolation media. Young colonies, but two to three days old, may develop masses of asci and ascospores on such media. It is obvious in most instances that yeasts cultured in the laboratory are on richer media than they had in their natural habitat from which they were isolated. On the other hand, many cultivated yeasts, particularly baker's and brewer's yeasts, as well as yeasts isolated from spoiled food or those which are found as contaminants in industrial fermentation processes, sporulate only with difficulty on media rich in nutrients. Special media have to be employed to induce a high percentage of the cells of these organisms to sporulate. The authors believe that the reason for finding so many heavily sporulating strains in a natural environment is because under such conditions cells containing ascospores survive better than vegetative cells. This greater resistance is probably due to the thick wall of the spores. Ascospores are more resistant to freezing, drying, exposure to harmful chemicals, and exposure to high temperatures. But, in contrast to the very heat-resistant bacterial spores, the heat resistance of ascospores is only 6°C to 12°C higher than that of vegetative cells under comparable conditions. It is actually more accurate to state that the death rate of a sporulated culture of yeast is lower than that of a vegetative culture. For example, Wickerham reported that four minutes at 58°C were sufficient to kill a vegetative culture of *Hansenula anomala,* but a sporulated culture still contained viable spores after ten minutes, although none were left after longer heating. In the same connection, Beijerinck, at about the turn of the century, demonstrated that yeasts which had been kept in collections for a long time and tended to lose the ability to sporulate could be reconverted into more heavily sporulating cultures. He did this by treating them with toxic agents, such as high concentrations of ethanol, which preferentially destroyed the vegetative cells over the sporulating forms. The tendency of some yeasts to lose the ability to form ascospores in culture over a period of years is well known, and may possibly be ascribed to more rapid growth of permanently asporogenous vegetative forms on laboratory media.

Numerous sporulation media and techniques have been described and advocated in the literature for the purpose of increasing the percentage of sporulating cells, in comparison to the normal cultivation media. Some authors have recommended first growing a yeast on a complex and rich pre-sporulation medium so that sporulation on special media is facilitated. A yeast culture must be young and well-nourished for effective sporulation to occur. Complex sporulation media (for example, a mixture of vegetable juices with or without autoclaved baker's yeast) have been devised for the purpose of satisfying the sporulation requirements for as many yeasts as possible. It must be acknowledged, however, that no sporulation medium can be called "universal." The compositions of a few special sporulation media are shown in the table (distilled water is used in all cases).

GORODKOWA AGAR		ACETATE AGAR	
	(%)		*(%)*
Meat extract	1	Bacto-Tryptose	0.25
Peptone	1	Glucose	0.062
Glucose	0.25	NaCl	0.062
NaCl	0.5	Na-acetate · $3H_2O$	0.5
Agar	2.0	Agar	2.0

YEAST AUTOLYSATE–GLUCOSE AGAR		POTATO–GLUCOSE AGAR	
	(%)		*(%)*
Yeast autolysate (dehydrated)	0.5	Potato extract*	(23 ml)
		Distilled water	(77 ml)
Glucose	5.0	Glucose	2
Agar	2.0	Agar	2

Of these, acetate agar is particularly effective for species of *Saccharomyces*, Gorodkowa agar for species of *Debaryomyces*,

*Potato extract is prepared by grinding 100 g of whole potato tissue. Add 300 ml water and store overnight in a refrigerator. Filter through cheese cloth and autoclave the filtrate.

potato extract glucose agar for certain haploid species of *Saccharomyces,* and yeast autolysate glucose medium for the production of asci in *Schwanniomyces* and related yeasts.

It is generally agreed that aerobic conditions are essential for sporulation, since few if any spores are formed under anaerobic (fermentative) conditions. A slightly reduced oxygen tension, however, appears to be very favorable in stimulating spore formation in the species of *Hanseniaspora* that produce asci with a single spheroidal spore. When these species are grown on potato glucose agar and part of the inoculum is covered with a coverslip, large numbers of asci usually develop under the coverslip in areas very close to the edge, but not in the aerobic uncovered portion of the growth (Fig. 11).

The pH of the media is not particularly critical but there appears to be an optimal range between pH 6 and 7. The temperature seems to be optimal in the normal ranges of room temperature, approximately 20–25°C.

The time required for sporulation to take place varies a great deal with species, variety, and even strain of yeast. Species freshly isolated from nature usually sporulate in one or two days, but strains held in culture for an extended period of time may require from one to several weeks before spore formation becomes apparent. For this reason, organisms on sporulation media should be investigated at frequent and regular intervals, for spores once formed may very well undergo germination on the same medium.

Taxonomic value of ascospores. The presence or absence of ascospore-forming ability determines whether a yeast is classified in the sporogenous or nonsporogenous yeasts. Ascospores formed by various yeasts exhibit a wide diversity of form, surface markings, size, color, number of spores per ascus, and presence

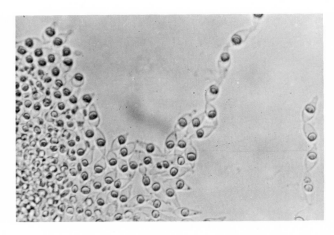

Fig. 11. Large numbers of asci of *Hanseniaspora uvarum* formed under reduced oxygen tension (see text for details).

of inclusion bodies (Fig. 12). Generally most of these features are quite constant for a given species. In some genera (for example *Nadsonia, Debaryomyces,* and *Schwanniomyces*) the respective species all have a similiar spore morphology, but in other genera (e.g. *Endomycopsis* and *Hansenula*) spore morphology varies among the species.

Fig. 12. Examples of ascospore shapes in yeast. From left to right: spheroidal, ovoidal, kidney- or bean-shaped, crescent- or sickle-shaped, hat-shaped, helmet-shaped, spheroidal with warty surface, walnut-shaped, saturn-shaped, spheroidal with spiny surface, arcuate, needle-shaped with appendage. Spores of certain species often contain lipid globules of various sizes. See text for examples of species containing these spores.

Spherical or short oval (globose) spores with a smooth surface are found in *Saccharomyces* and other genera (Fig. 13a, b). Spores with the shape of a kidney bean are characteristic in *Fabospora*. *Endomycopsis selenospora* forms spores which are crescent- or sickle-shaped. Long, thin, needle-shaped spores with a non-motile whip-like appendage are found in *Nematospora,* while arcuate spores are formed by *Eremothecium* (Fig. 13c).

There are also spores that have a ledge, or brim, which surrounds the spores. The degree of prominence of the brim and its position on the spore vary widely. Those with a helmet-shape have short, thin brims, nearly tangential to the spore surface (*Pichia*). Sometimes the ledge is so low that the spore may appear hemispherical. A more pronounced brim, slightly curved, gives the spore the appearance of a typical derby hat (*Hansenula*) (Fig. 13d). Another type of spore found in *Hansenula* is Saturn-

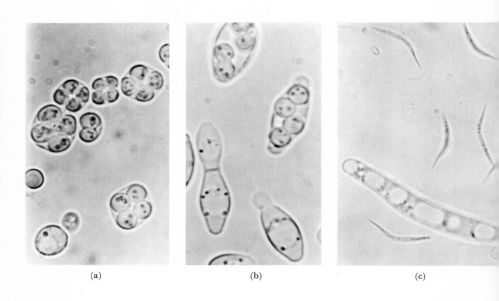

(a)   (b)   (c)

Fig. 13.   Asci and ascospores of yeast: (a) spheroidal spores,
2—4 per ascus in a diploid *Saccharomyes* species; (b) an ascus
with two pairs of spheroidal spores in *Saccharomycodes ludwigii;*
in one ascus two spores are conjugating (see p. 40); the refractile granules are presumably polyphosphate storage products; (c) arcuate spores of *Eremothecium ashbyi;* (d) asci and liberated spores in *Hansenula anomala;* the spore shape resembles a

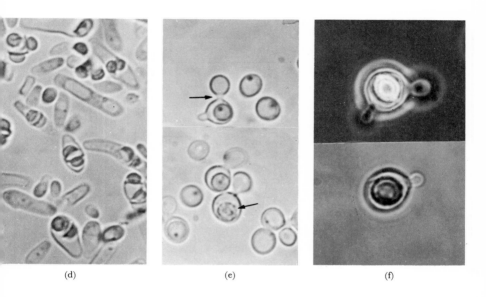

(d)   (e)   (f)

derby hat; (e) asci of *Debaryomyces hansenii* with a single (usually) warty, spheroidal spore. Note fusion between two cells or between a cell and a bud; (f) asci of a *Schwanniomyces* species with walnut-shaped spores. Note difference of appearance of spore when observed under phase contrast (top) and bright-field illumination.

shaped. This smooth-walled spore has an equatorial ledge causing it to resemble the planet Saturn.

The surface topography of a spore may show other interesting features. The spores of *Nadsonia* are spiny, those of *Debaryomyces* and *Citeromyces* irregular or warty (Fig. 13e), and spores of *Schwanniomyces* resemble a walnut (Fig. 13f).

Spores are generally without color (hyaline), although due to their refractile nature they sometimes appear slightly greenish under the light microscope. In some genera the spores are amber to brownish in color (*Nadsonia* and *Lipomyces*), which is evident upon microscopic observation. In some species of other genera, colonies of heavily sporulating strains appear light pink to reddish-brown, but the color of individual spores is not sufficiently pronounced to be apparent under the microscope. This is found quite often in the genus *Fabospora* and less frequently in *Pichia* and *Hansenula*.

The number of spores per ascus may vary for a particular species, although the majority of the yeasts form a definite maximum number of spores in each ascus. In some yeasts the maximum number is eight *(Schizosaccharomyces octosporus,* Fig. 14), but in most yeasts it is four *(Saccharomyces cerevisiae),* although asci with two or three spores in this group are quite common. There are also yeasts which as a rule produce only one or, more rarely, two spores per ascus (*Debaryomyces*). Yeasts with indefinite numbers of spores are also known. For example, *Lipomyces* produces a variable number ranging from 4 to 16 and occasionally more. *Kluyveromyces polysporus* has asci often containing 64 spores or more.

The authors prefer to observe sporulation and ascospore morphology in wet mounts of living material. Although ascospores can be stained with malachite green and other basic dyes, certain morphological details are lost during the staining process. Furthermore, the ability of yeast spores to retain the dye varies considerably with the species and the age of the spores.

All of these characteristic features, including the manner of ascus formation are of great taxonomic value in separating genera and in some cases even species within a genus.

Heterothallism and sporulation. Heterothallism occurs quite commonly in yeast. Many yeasts have been known for years as imperfect species in the order *Cryptococcales* because ascospore formation had never been detected. In more recent years, however, it has been found that upon mixing of several strains of the same species sporulation did occur in some instances. This is dependent upon the presence of appropriate mating types in the mixture of the several strains. Hence, if spores do not form on sporulation media it may be essential to isolate several additional strains of the same organism, so these can then be mixed and placed on sporulation media in the hope of finding mating types. In this way it has been found that many species of *Torulopsis* and *Candida* now have known perfect forms among the sporogenous yeasts. While the occurrence of heterothallism in yeast is a recent observation, its occurrence in other fungi belonging to the *Phycomycetes, Ascomycetes,* and *Basidiomycetes* has been known for many years. Its discovery among the yeasts (which belong to the lower *Ascomycetes*) is therefore not surprising.

The mating reaction between naturally occurring heterothallic types is quite variable. Sometimes the reaction is so strong that it is preceded by a pronounced agglutination between cells of opposite mating types, and this is followed by zygote formation. With other species, however, the mating reaction may

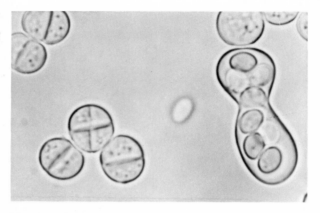

Fig. 14. Vegetative cells and an eight-spored ascus of *Schizosaccharomyces octosporus* (note that not all of the spores are in the same plane of focus).

be very weak and difficult to detect. In such cases, in which incompatibility factors may be present in the mating types, it is very helpful to prepare mutants of the mating types which have a nutritional deficiency. This can be done by treatment of the cultures with ultraviolet light. Suppose we have mixed on a sporulation medium one mating type requiring adenine and another requiring L-arginine for growth. After sufficient incubation the mixture can be streaked on a synthetic medium which contains neither adenine nor arginine. Only zygotes will grow on the "minimal" medium, because each partner supplies what the other lacks. In this way one zygote can be detected and isolated among a million or more nonsporulating cells and sporulation of the diploid zygote (or of its offspring) can be conveniently studied.

It will be noted from the foregoing discussion and from what will follow in the next chapter on the genetics of yeast that sexual differentiation in yeasts does not imply that yeast has reproductive structures to which the terms male and female gametes can be applied. The term gamete is normally reserved for highly differentiated male and female fusion cells rather than for the relatively unspecialized vegetative cells or ascospores of yeast. Nevertheless, conjugating yeast cells, or ascospores, are often designated as gametes, especially if the gametes represent different mating types. Because such gametes are not differentiated morphologically into male and female structures, they are usually designated as a and α, or as $+$ and $-$. The fusion of haploid, homothallic cells, prior to sporulation, may be considered as a case of somatic conjugation.

Sporulation is undoubtedly the most important biological event from the standpoint of the yeast itself, since it governs to a large extent the evolutionary development of the various groups in their phylogenetic lines. From the standpoint of the investigator, yeast sporulation has made possible genetic studies, and it is one of the principal foundations upon which yeast taxonomy is based. In spite of occasional difficulties encountered in the study of sporulation, its importance more than justifies the time invested in trying to establish sporulation conditions for cultures isolated from various sources. Finally, the observation of sporulating yeast and ascospores is indeed a thrilling experience in the study of yeast.

V / Yeast Genetics

Although the formation of ascospores in yeast was already recognized during the middle of the nineteenth century, sporulation in *Saccharomyces* was thought to be associated with some type of parthenogenetic process, a term found over and over again in the older literature and even occasionally today. In parthenogenesis, best known in some members of the insects and crustacea, sexual reproduction can occur with only one sex cell (the female egg) involved, the male gamete being absent. It was believed that such a process occurred in diploid yeasts, such as *Saccharomyces cerevisiae*, since no evidence of a sexual conjugation was known to take place. The true significance of ascospore formation in yeast was discovered independently by Satava in Czechoslovakia and Winge in Denmark during the years 1934–1935. The fundamental discoveries of these investigators established that in *Saccharomyces* a true alternation of generations occurs. This means that the vegetative cells of the yeast are diploid (containing the 2 n number of chromosomes), whereas the ascospores were found to be haploid and contain 1 n chromosomes. By a fusion process (conjugation) between the ascospores or their progeny, the diplophase was re-established. This discovery of alternation of haplophase and diplophase in yeast, similar to the life cycles of higher organisms, made it possible to initiate fruitful genetic studies with yeasts. Cultures resulting from single ascospores can be used for investigations on segregation, mutation, and hybridization, especially since ascospores of many strains of yeast remain haploid when allowed to germinate individually.

Winge and his collaborators developed techniques for isolating the four ascospores of strains of *Saccharomyces cerevisiae* by use of a micromanipulator. By observing and comparing giant colonies produced when isolated spores were allowed to grow on malt gelatin media, genetic segregation was shown to occur in the genus *Saccharomyces*. In these early days of yeast genetics, Winge and his co-workers were able to show that it is possible to hybridize spores produced by two different species of *Saccharomyces*. They placed a spore from one species and that from another side by side in a droplet of medium and when they grew together (conjugated) they produced a diploid offspring, representing a hybrid. It was shown that if one of the parents fermented a certain sugar and the other did not do so, the hybrid was always able to ferment this sugar. In other words, the ability to ferment sugars was found to be a dominant character. Another way of saying this is that the gene responsible for the synthesis of a specific hydrolytic enzyme (necessary for the hydrolysis of a disaccharide to be fermented) is dominant in the F_1 generation.

Another great step forward was the fundamental discovery by the American investigator Lindegren, in 1943, that heterothallism exists in *Saccharomyces*. He discovered that in many strains of *Saccharomyces cerevisiae,* two of the ascospores belong to one mating type and the other two to another mating type, usually referred to as *a* and α. This $2:2$ segregation indicates that mating is controlled by a single gene. Lindegren found that if the *a* and α spores were allowed to germinate separately from each other they developed into haploid clones, or populations. However, upon mixing of *a* and *α* populations, conjugation between the cells of opposite mating types occurred rapidly and the diplophase was re-established. The finding of haploid clones of opposite mating types has greatly facilitated genetic studies with yeast, because it now became possible to do many hybridizations with the offspring of one single ascospore.

Two complications in this technique of hybridization have been encountered. One is the possibility that members of a haploid population may conjugate with cells of their own mating type, forming a homothallic diploid yeast. This is called selfing or self-diploidization. Another problem is that mutations have been observed from one mating type to the other. If this occurs in a haploid population, hybridization or conjugation between the mutated mating type and the original mating type results in diploid cells. Such diploids may be different from those obtained when the mating is conducted with a regular strain of opposite mating type. These disadvantages have been overcome, however, by the use of biochemical mutants, in which the haploid populations are not only labeled by mating type but, in addition, by inducing one or more nutritional deficiencies (markers), such as a requirement for a purine or some amino acid. For example, a mutant that is recessive for adenine synthesis can be crossed with another haploid strain of opposite mating type, which requires L-arginine for growth; this will yield a hybrid which can grow in a minimal medium devoid of both adenine and L-arginine. But if the diploid had resulted from selfing, or mating-type mutation, it would not grow in the minimal medium.

A large amount of work was subsequently done on the segregational behavior of the individual ascospores of various yeast hybrids and of naturally occurring diploid yeasts. In many cases when a fermenter of a certain sugar was hybridized with a nonfermenter, thus producing a diploid yeast, the four asco-spores, upon sporulation of the hybrid, showed a 2:2 segregation. In such a segregation two of the ascospores produced cultures that were able to ferment the sugar in question and the other two were unable to do so. This indicated that a single gene was responsible for the fermentation of the sugar or, more pre-cisely, responsible for synthesis of an enzyme necessary for the hydrolysis of the disaccharide sugar involved. Similarly, the inheritance of the genes involved in vitamin synthesis often followed this pattern. Thus, when a yeast which required a certain vitamin was hybridized with one not requiring it, the hybrid segregated out 2:2 upon subsequent sporulation. The deficiency in the synthesis of these vitamins appears to be con-trolled by a single gene. When one of the conjugating partners can ferment two sugars (represented, for example, as F_1F_2) and the other partner cannot do so (f_1f_2), the hybrid ($F_1f_1F_2f_2$) will ferment both. If the hybrid sporulates, the abilities to fer-ment the two sugars are usually segregated independently from each other, although each one in a 2:2 ratio. In some cases it has been observed that certain combinations of characters seg-regate as if they were one unit. This means that the genes re-sponsible for these properties are located close together on the same chromosome, a phenomenon called linkage. For example, in *Saccharomyces* the gene M_1 and R_1 (two genes responsible for the fermentation of maltose and raffinose, respectively) move as a single unit during reduction division and hybridizations.

A major controversy followed, however, when it was observed that in some hybrids, upon analyses of *many* asci, some asci segre-gated 2:2, some 3:1 (3 fermenters to 1 nonfermenter), and some segregated out 4:0, in which all four ascospores were able to ferment the particular sugar. Through the painstaking researches of Winge and Roberts it has become apparent that in some cases the fermentation of certain sugars, such as maltose, is controlled by more than a single gene (polymeric genes). They concluded that *Saccharomyces cerevisiae* contains at least three nonlinked polymeric genes, M_1, M_2, and M_3, for the production of maltase. The term nonlinked signifies that the genes in question move independently. Allowing for the phenomenon of crossing-over between chromosomes and independent segregation of these three genes, good correlation was found between the calculated and actual numbers of asci giving 2:2, 3:1, and 4:0 segregations upon experimental analysis. It should be emphasized that not all species contain polymeric genes for the fermentation of maltose. For example, the yeast *Saccharomyces italicus* contains only a single gene for the fermentation of maltose and during sporulation only 2:2 segregations are obtained.

Winge and Roberts proved their hypothesis of polymeric genes through an elaborate series of hybridizations. Through crossings and back-crossings they were able to separate the various maltase genes and to obtain strains of yeast which contained only the M_1, or the M_2, or the M_3 gene. Later, additional nonlinked M genes have been found, so that at least six maltase genes are now known in *Saccharomyces*. Polymeric genes also occur with respect to the fermentation of certain other sugars, for example sucrose and raffinose. The significance of these genes has become clearer in recent years. Through the studies of Halverson and collaborators it was found that the proteins, representing the various maltases controlled by the different M genes, apparently have identical properties. A very interesting effect of gene dosage has also been found, namely a yeast with a single M gene produces less maltase enzyme than a yeast with two or more M genes. In fact, the effect of gene dosage was approximately additive.

As a result of all this work, the inheritance of fermentative properties may be said to obey Mendelian laws. Thus, if a haploid yeast containing only the M_1 gene is crossed with a haploid yeast containing the recessive m_1 gene, the resulting hybrid has the formula M_1m_1. After reduction division and sporulation the four spores segregate out into two maltose fermenters and two non-maltose fermenters, a normal Mendelian segregation. Reduction division, or meiosis, has also been followed cytologically by staining techniques, and formation of four nuclei from the original diploid nucleus has been demonstrated clearly. Occasionally one or more of the nuclei divide once again, and ultimately eight or sometimes as many as ten or twelve nuclei are formed. This may result in asci with five to twelve spores, as has been observed in certain strains of *Saccharomyces* species. These extra divisions of the nuclei are termed supernumerary mitoses.

Another result of this phenomenon is that occasionally an ascospore may contain two nuclei. As an example, a yeast of the genetic formula M_1m_1 undergoes reduction division. Initially four nuclei are produced which consist of two M_1 nuclei and two m_1 nuclei. Now suppose that the two nuclei characterized by M_1 divide once more and that the two extra M_1 nuclei become associated with the m_1 nuclei. If these pairs become incorporated into the spores formed, the result would be two haploid spores containing an M_1 gene and two "diploid" spores containing paired M_1 and m_1 nuclei. This gives rise to an irregular segregation, since now all spores upon isolation would give clones that ferment maltose, whereas on the premise of the original yeast, which was heterozygous for maltase, a $2:2$ segregation would be expected. These exceptions are fortunately rather rare and they can be recognized with proper care.

Still another interesting phenomenon related to the problem of irregular segregation is the now well-established property of yeast that clones with a ploidy higher than 2 n can be formed. In other words, triploid, tetraploid, and even higher ploidy are known to exist in yeasts. Let us take a simple example in which a cross is to be made between a haploid strain of mating type *a* and another yeast of presumed mating type α. It has been explained above that occasionally mating types may conjugate with themselves and this process of selfing produces a diploid yeast of formula αα. If crossing is now attempted, namely, that of the haploid strain *a* with a diploid αα strain, fusion or conjugation may occur, resulting in a triploid yeast of the formula *a*αα. It is obvious that in a sporulating triploid yeast segregations are quite different from the expected 2:2 ratio in a diploid hybrid. Moreover, it has been found that the spores of a triploid yeast are characteristically of low viability. In contrast, the spores of a tetraploid have a high viability. Such a yeast may be obtained by crossing a diploid *aa* with a diploid αα, yielding the tetraploid *aa*αα. It is now known that some irregular segregations observed by various investigators must be ascribed to the occurrence of yeast of higher ploidy among the experimental material. An interesting observation is the finding that the average volume of yeast cells is a linear function of the degree of ploidy in the range of haploid to hexaploid forms.

Finally, consideration should be given to the phenomenon of genic conversion, first invoked by Lindegren as an explanation of irregular segregation in yeast and later studied in detail by Mortimer. Briefly, genic conversion differs from crossing-over during meiosis in that during the latter process a reciprocal recombination of genetic markers occurs, whereas in the former the process is usually nonreciprocal. Mortimer found that the frequency of irregular segregation due to genic conversion was different for different allelic pairs. For the great majority of loci (allelic pairs) segregations averaged approximately 1% 3:1, 98% 2:2, and 1% 1:3, although for some loci the percentages of 3:1 and 1:3 were significantly higher. The expected ratio, in the absence of genic conversion, would have been 100% 2:2 segregations. The mechanism of genic conversion is still unknown, and the exact relationship between conversion and crossing-over remains uncertain.

Much of the current work in yeast genetics is concerned with the genetic behavior of the genes responsible for certain biochemical properties. Many mutants have been prepared, particularly those which are called auxotrophs—those yeasts deficient in the ability to carry out some intermediate step in the synthesis of an essential amino acid or of a pyrimidine or purine base. Work with these mutants, in turn, has led to a study of the location of these genes on the various chromosomes, and an extensive chromosome-mapping program is now well under way by a number of geneticists. On the basis of these studies it is now clear that a haploid *Saccharomyces* yeast contains at least 14 to 15 individual chromosomes and thus a normal diploid yeast would have 28 to 30 chromosomes. To map chromosomes a large number of mutant yeast stocks have been built up for many years. One of the goals of chromosome-mapping is to determine among a group of mutually linked genes the order in which they appear along the chromosome. This is basically done by crossing parental types differing in one or more characters and statistically analyzing the segregants. For example, in a three-factor cross, ABC × abc, it is possible to determine which of the three genes lying near one another upon a single chromosome is between the other two. The fact that biochemical gene markers do not tend to interfere with each other nearly so frequently as morphological markers makes yeasts especially suitable for genetic analysis.

Mention should be made of a very special type of biochemical mutation, namely, the loss of respiratory activity. Many kinds of yeast, including all species of *Saccharomyces*, possess both the respiratory pathway of metabolism (substrate combustion by oxygen consumption) as well as the fermentative pathway (alcoholic fermentation). The fundamental investigations of Ephrussi and his collaborators have shown that in a normal population of baker's yeast approximately 1% of the cells are abnormal in that they do not possess the ability to respire. When isolated, these abnormal cells represent a stable mutant type, because after many tranfers the respiration deficiency is still present. Because the energy derived from fermentation is less extensive than that from respiration, the colonies produced by these respiration-deficient (RD) yeasts are smaller than those of normal types and have been called "petites" or small colonies by Ephrussi. This respiration deficiency was shown to be caused by the lack of several respiratory enzymes and has been traced to the loss of certain self-duplicating particles in the cytoplasm of the yeast. When haploid spores of a RD mutant are crossed with normal haploid yeasts of opposite mating types, respiration is ordinarily re-established because the normal mating type reintroduces the lost cytoplasmic self-duplicating particles. When the hybrid formed in this way is allowed to sporulate, all of the four spores form clones of normal respiratory yeast. Thus, cytoplasmic inheritance is quite different from that controlled by nuclear genes.

It was subsequently established that respiration in yeast is actually controlled by two factors, a nuclear gene plus cytoplasmic self-duplicating particles. For respiration to occur, both must be present, whereas the absence of either one results in loss of respiratory activity. Although respiration deficiency occurs at a low rate in normal populations of yeast, its frequency can be tremendously increased when yeast is grown in the presence of certain dyes or heavy metal solutions. Under appropriate conditions a normal clone can be very rapidly transformed into a nonrespiratory population.

The mutants devoid of cytoplasmic particles are usually designated as vegetative mutants, whereas those controlled by mutation at a particular gene locus are called segregational mutants. Spectroscopic examination of intact cells of vegetative mutants has revealed the absence of the cytochromes a, a_3 and b. The absence of these cytochromes can account for the absence of several corresponding enzymatic activities in the yeast cell. The segregational mutants, on the other hand, result from single gene mutations which can be induced by treatment with ultraviolet light or other mutagenic agents. The segregational mutants, therefore, show a normal Mendelian (2:2) segregation following crossing with normal strains.

There has been much interest in the nature of the cytoplasmic particles involved in respiration and in their modification in RD mutants. It has been well established by the work of Linnane and others that purified cell-free mitochondrial particles of normal baker's yeast contain the enzymes of the citric acid cycle and are able to cause oxidative phosphorylation with suitable substrates. It was originally believed, therefore, that in vegetative RD mutants, mitochondria would be absent. However, recent work by Linnane, Schatz, and others, has shown that "petite" mutants do contain mitochondria, which still contain the several enzymes of the citric acid cycle, but are lacking in the cytochromes b, a, and a_3. As a result of the loss of these cytochromes the cell is unable to carry out oxidations by the electron transport system. In addition, upon isolation, the mitochondria of the RD mutants appear to be more labile than those of the wild type and in electron micrographs of ultrathin sections they give the appearance of having a less highly organized internal structure.

Studies of respiration deficiency have gone far beyond what is possible to cover in this short space. The same applies to other aspects of genetic investigations in yeast. It is truly remarkable that in a period of thirty years yeast genetics has developed into a highly specialized science and has made important contributions of fundamental importance to biology.

VI / Metabolic Activities of Yeast

Although the yeasts as a group are not as diversified as bacteria in their metabolism, one finds appreciable differences in metabolic patterns, substrates which can be utilized, and end products produced.

Yeast is most commonly thought of as a fermentative organism, in the sense that it can carry out the well-known alcoholic fermentation, expressed by the equation $C_6H_{12}O_6 \rightarrow 2C_2H_5OH + 2CO_2$. The reason for this notion is probably that so much work has been done with baker's and brewer's yeast, both strongly fermentative species of *Saccharomyces*. It must be kept in mind, however, that *Saccharomyces cerevisiae* also possesses a pronounced respiratory metabolism. In other words, in the presence of oxygen it has the ability to respire or oxidize glucose to CO_2 and water. Depending on the conditions of growth, *S. cerevisiae*, therefore, can shift its metabolism from a fermentative to an oxidative pathway; both systems yield energy to the cell, although the latter far more than the former. Pasteur was the first to demonstrate that a fermenting yeast, when subjected to aeration, decreases its fermentative activity, and part of the glucose is respired to CO_2 and water. This phenomenon, which bears the name "Pasteur effect," has received a practical application in the production of baker's yeast where alcohol formation is not desirable. When the sugar concentration is kept low, highly aerobic conditions cause all of the sugar to be respired to the above-mentioned end products.

There are also many species of yeast which are entirely aerobic, and such yeasts lack the ability to cause alcoholic fermentation. Examples of yeasts in this category are all of the species of *Rhodotorula* and *Cryptococcus*, and some species of *Candida, Torulopsis,* and of certain other genera. In addition, there are intermediary types with a strongly respiratory and a weakly fermentative metabolism, represented by several species of the genera *Debaryomyces* and *Pichia*. The reverse is also found — namely, that a yeast has a relatively weak respiratory activity, but is strongly fermentative. This situation is exemplified by *Saccharomyces carlsbergensis*, a yeast used for the fermentation of lager beers.

We shall now briefly consider certain aspects of the fermentation process of yeast. When glucose is added to a suspension of *Saccharomyces cerevisiae*, the sugar enters the cell with the aid of a transport system built in the cell wall or in the cytoplasmic membrane. Once it has entered the cell, the sugar is phosphorylated to glucose-6-phosphate with the aid of yeast hexokinase and adenosine triphosphate (ATP). This is followed by a degradation, via the well-known Embden-Meyerhof pathway of glycolysis, to two molecules of pyruvate. The two molecules of pyruvate are decarboxylated, giving two molecules of CO_2 and two molecules of acetaldehyde; the latter are subsequently reduced to two molecules of ethanol with the aid of reduced coenzymes. The coenzyme involved in alcoholic fermentation is nicotinic acid adenine dinucleotide (NAD), which had become reduced to $NADH_2$ during an earlier intermediary step. The over-all result of the degradation of glucose is two molecules of CO_2, and two molecules of ethanol. In addition, during the process a net gain of two moles of ATP (high-energy phosphate) is realized, which is used for purposes of cell growth and synthesis. In the absence of a source of nitrogen (when the yeast cannot grow), part of the glucose is assimilated by the yeast in the form of reserve storage products. A suspension of resting cells of *S. cerevisiae* in phosphate buffer with glucose as the carbon source converts about 70% of the glucose to CO_2 and alcohol, whereas the remaining 30% is assimilated into storage products at the time the free glucose of the medium is used up. Upon longer incubation the storage products can subsequently be utilized slowly by endogenous fermentation.

Many years ago Kluyver established three basic fermentation rules which, to a large extent, still hold. His first rule was that if a yeast does not ferment D-glucose it will not ferment any other sugar. The second rule is that if yeast ferments D-glucose it will also ferment D-fructose and D-mannose (but not necessarily D-galactose). Thirdly, if a yeast ferments maltose it does not ferment lactose, and vice versa. Only very few exceptions to the last rule have been discovered; for example, the ale yeast *Brettanomyces claussenii* will ferment both maltose and lactose.

The reasons behind these observations are essentially as follows: In the fermentation of di-, tri-, or polysaccharides the fermentation always goes through the hexose stage. Hydrolytic enzymes at the cell surface or located internally break down these carbohydrates to hexose sugars. Thus, if hexose sugars are not fermented, oligosaccharides are not fermented either. Secondly, it has been found that the three sugars, D-glucose, D-fructose and D-mannose, are all phosphorylated by the same enzyme, yeast hexokinase, to the respective hexose-6-phosphates. Both glucose-6- and mannose-6-phosphate are then transformed into the common denominator, fructose-6-phosphate. D-galactose, however, is phosphorylated to galactose-1-phosphate by a separate enzyme, galactokinase. The utilization of galactose involves at least three additional preliminary steps after which galactose joins the normal sugar pathway. The absence of galactokinase and other necessary enzymes is the reason why many yeasts which can ferment the first three sugars cannot ferment galactose.

Enzymes for the hydrolysis of sucrose, melibiose, raffinose, inulin, and starch are located at the cell surface, and hence these carbohydrates are broken down before they enter the cell as hexoses. On the other hand, maltose and lactose are hydrolyzed inside the cell, after being transported across the membrane as disaccharides. It is not uncommon that a yeast grown on glucose has a very low level of the enzymes necessary to hydrolyze di-, tri-, and polysaccharides. Such yeasts must first be adapted by growing them in media containing the respective sugars serving as inducers for the synthesis of the necessary hydrolytic enzymes.

Although the number of species of yeast which can ferment hexoses, disaccharides, and trisaccharides is large, yeasts which are able to ferment polysaccharides, such as inulin and starch, are relatively rare. *Saccharomyces fragilis* is an example of a yeast which ferments inulin well, and *Endomycopsis fibuligera* is an example of one which can ferment starch fairly well. Sugars most commonly fermented by yeasts are glucose, galactose, maltose, sucrose, lactose, trehalose, melibiose, and raffinose. Yeasts have also been found which can ferment melezitose (a trisaccharide), the disaccharide cellobiose, or α-methyl-D-glucoside. Relatively little information is known about the ability of yeasts to ferment the more rarely found di- and trisaccharides.

No yeasts have ever been found which can ferment pentose sugars or methyl pentoses, although many yeasts can utilize these compounds very well by a respiratory pathway. In this connection it should be pointed out that sugars such as cellobiose, which are not normally fermented well, often are good substrates for growth through the respiratory process.

The total amount of ethanol which a yeast can produce by fermentation varies considerably with the strain. With suitable strains and a sufficient supply of sugar, an alcohol concentration of 12–14% by volume is obtained relatively rapidly, but the higher the alcohol content becomes, the slower the fermentation progresses. Fermentations have been recorded in which 18–19% alcohol by volume was produced. These fermentations are rather unpredictable, and such high alcohol levels can be achieved only with certain yeast strains after many months and under special conditions of temperature and sugar concentration.

The respiratory activity of yeast has been studied over many decades by some of the outstanding biochemists of the century, such as Warburg, Wieland, Keilin, Krebs, Kornberg, and many others. The respiratory pathways which have been shown to exist in yeast include the well-known citric acid cycle, or tricarboxylic acid (TCA) cycle, and its more recently discovered variation, the so-called glyoxylate cycle. The latter cycle accounts for the fact that so many yeasts can grow abundantly on two-carbon compounds, as ethanol or acetate. Since the TCA cycle eliminates two molecules of CO_2 during each cycle, ethanol or acetate would not allow growth (carbon assimilation) by the yeast if the TCA cycle were the exclusive pathway.

A third cycle known to exist in yeast is the so-called pentose cycle, or the hexosemonophosphate shunt mechanism, in which glucose, after being phosphorylated in the usual way to glucose-6-phosphate, is initially oxidized to 6-phosphogluconic acid. This cycle and the glyoxylate cycle, the details of which can be found in the standard biochemistry textbooks, have an important bearing on the production of certain by-products, which are mentioned below.

Although much of the initial work on respiratory activity in yeast has been done with hexose sugars, a much greater array of substrates is available for respiration than for fermentation. Thus, pentose sugars, methyl pentoses, sugar alcohols, organic acids and many other compounds have been studied as substrates for yeast respiration. The ability or inability of yeast to utilize representative carbon compounds for growth has become one of the most valuable criteria in the differentiation of species of yeast. Growth experiments with certain yeasts, such as species of *Cryptococcus*, have shown that very frequently the pentoses (D-xylose, L-arabinose, and occasionally D-arabinose) are much better substrates for growth than is D-glucose. This preference for pentoses is probably related to their habitat in nature, where these sugars are more prevalent than hexose sugars.

By-products. We shall now consider some of the by-products of yeast metabolism. Since quantitatively and qualitatively these products are often very different under anaerobic and aerobic conditions, it seems best to discuss the products separately under the two environmental conditions.

Under fermentative conditions ethanol and CO_2 account for nearly 95% of the glucose fermented. Yeast also produces small amounts of glycerol, succinic acid, higher alcohols (fusel alcohols), 2,3-butanediol, and traces of acetaldehyde, acetic acid, and lactic acid. Glycerol is quantitatively the most important by-product and results from the enzymatic reduction of dihydroxyacetone phosphate, an intermediate in the pathway of alcoholic fermentation.

The production of higher alcohols during fermentation has been studied extensively, probably because of the effect of these alcohols on the quality of alcoholic beverages, especially distilled ones. Fusel oil is produced in very small amounts by all strains of yeast that have been investigated. The major components are isoamyl, optically active amyl, isobutyl, and *n*-propyl alcohols, and a minor component is *n*-butyl alcohol. The classical studies of Ehrlich at the beginning of the century showed that yeasts can convert amino acids to higher alcohols by the elimination of ammonia and CO_2, finally forming an alcohol with one carbon atom less than the amino acid contained. Examples are the conversion of leucine to isoamyl alcohol and isoleucine to active amyl alcohol.

$$\underset{\underset{COOH}{|}}{\overset{\overset{R}{|}}{CHNH_2}} \xrightarrow[\text{transaminase}]{NH_3} \underset{\underset{COOH}{|}}{\overset{\overset{R}{|}}{C=O}} \xrightarrow[\text{carboxylase}]{} \underset{+CO_2}{\overset{\overset{R}{|}}{CHO}} \xrightarrow[\text{reduction}]{NADH_2} \overset{\overset{R}{|}}{CH_2OH}$$

Quite recently, however, it has been shown that all of the components of fusel oil listed above are also produced from glucose in the absence of amino acids. Here they arise through intermediates in the biosynthesis of the three amino acids, leucine, isoleucine, and valine, probably by a "shunt" or overflow mechanism.

Under aerobic conditions of growth, a number of by-products have been found in surprisingly high concentrations. In addition, the nature of the products varies greatly with the species of yeast. A brief mention of these products will be made.

Species of the genus *Brettanomyces* produce large amounts of acetic acid from glucose or ethanol, an incomplete oxidation process of these substrates. The concentration of acetic acid may become so great that the yeast is rapidly killed off unless adequate buffering by calcium carbonate is provided. Acetic acid is also produced in large amounts by certain species of *Hansenula*, such as *Hansenula anomala*, but in this case the acetic acid becomes enzymatically bound to ethanol in the form of ethyl acetate. This product can be synthesized in very high yields from glucose or alcohol by this yeast, provided the pH of the medium is not too high. In *H. anomala*, ethyl acetate is a transitory by-product, because upon longer incubation and aeration this ester is used up by the yeast. Many esters of as yet unknown composition have been detected in media inoculated with different species of yeast, mainly on the basis of striking odors and aromas.

Under aerobic conditions the amount of succinic acid is greatly increased. This can be attributed to the participation of the glyoxylate cycle in which the following reaction accounts schematically for this increase: $2CH_3COOH$ (acetyl) $\rightarrow$ $COOH \cdot CH_2 \cdot CH_2 \cdot COOH + [2H]$.

Another nonvolatile acid is produced by *Kloeckera brevis*, *Hansenula subpelliculosa*, *Trichosporon capitatum*, and several others. This acid, which has been named zymonic acid, is a cyclic tetronic acid; in the presence of sufficient calcium carbonate some of these yeasts can convert about half of the glucose utilized to this acid.

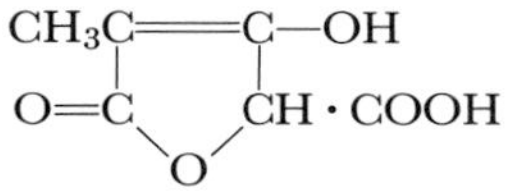

Zymonic acid

Many of the haploid species of *Saccharomyces* and imperfect yeasts belonging to *Torulopsis* and *Candida* can produce very high yields of polyhydric alcohols from glucose. These include glycerol, erythritol, D-arabitol, and D-mannitol. These compounds are produced only under highly aerobic conditions; anaerobically ethanol and CO_2 are the products. These compounds are related to the intermediate products of the pentose cycle. The formation of these products varies qualitatively and quantitatively with the species of yeast (see also Chapter X). Low levels of inorganic phosphate stimulate production of these polyhydric alcohols.

Very interesting by-products have been found in the culture fluid of the yeast *Torulopsis magnoliae*, which produces, in heavily aerated cultures, an extracellular hydroxy fatty acid glycoside of the sugar sophorose, a sugar in which two glucose molecules are linked by a β-1,2 bond. This heavier-than-water glycolipid is an oily liquid which collects at the bottom of the flask after the aerated medium comes to rest. The lipid part consists of 17-hydroxy saturated or unsaturated fatty acids with 18 carbon atoms. Yields of these glycolipids can be greatly increased by adding to the medium normal fatty acids or even hydrocarbons, which the yeast is apparently able to oxidize to fatty acids.

Another interesting extracellular lipid has been discovered in the culture fluid of certain species of *Rhodotorula* and of the yeast *Candida bogoriensis*. The products, which may appear as needle-shaped crystals at the bottom of the culture flask, consist of a fatty acid and a polyol, in other words, another glycolipid type. Here, polyols are represented by D-mannitol, D-arabitol, and xylitol, the latter in minor amounts. The fatty acid portion consists of 3-D-hydroxystearic acid. An unidentified species of yeast has been shown to produce still another kind of extracellular lipid, namely 8, 9, 13-triacetoxydocosanoic acid.

Another class of lipid materials is produced by certain species of *Hansenula*, namely, those which form mat, dull colonies and pellicles in liquid media. This class comprises the sphingolipids, which were discovered quite recently by Wickerham and Stodola in *Hansenula ciferrii*. In suitable strains of this yeast, extracellular microcrystals of sphingolipids are found among the cells. Between one and two percent of the glucose supplied can be transformed into sphingolipid under optimal conditions. The most abundant component is tetraacetylphytosphingosine, containing a long hydrocarbon chain to which are attached three O-acetyl groups and one N-acetyl group.

$$CH_3(CH_2)_{13}\overset{\displaystyle OCOCH_3}{\underset{\displaystyle |}{CH}}\text{------}\overset{\displaystyle OCOCH_3}{\underset{\displaystyle |}{CH}}\text{------}\overset{\displaystyle NH\cdot COCH_3}{\underset{\displaystyle |}{CH}}\text{------------}CH_2OCOCH_3$$

Tetraacetylphytosphingosine

A minor component of yeast sphingolipid has recently been identified as triacetyl dihydrosphingosine.

Pigments of yeast. Although the colonies of most species of yeast appear white, or white with a slight greyish or yellowish cast, carotenoid pigments are produced by species of one genus of the ballistosporic yeasts (*Sporobolomyces*) and of two genera of asporogenous yeasts (*Rhodotorula* and *Cryptococcus*). *Rhodotorula* species produce sufficient pigments so that the colonies assume various shades of red and yellow, often very bright in color. Species of *Cryptococcus* usually synthesize smaller amounts and, as a result, their colonies are often only slightly yellowish or pinkish or even nearly colorless. Carotenoids produced by pink species of *Rhodotorula* are composed mainly of two oxygenated compounds, torulin and torularhodin. The concentrations of these pigments relative to each other vary greatly in different species and strains. The yellow color of some species of *Rhodotorula* and *Cryptococcus* results primarily from the production of β-carotene in the absence of pink pigments. Minor amounts of several other pigments have been demonstrated, for example γ-carotene and lycopene. The last one is well known from its prominence in tomato fruits.

The pigment concentration is always small. The yellow-colored yeasts attributed to the genus *Rhodotorula* contain about 6 to 10 mg β-carotene per 100 g dry weight of yeast. The pink species of *Rhodotorula* tested by Nakayama had a total pigment content of 3 to 17 mg per 100 g, of which 15 to 43% was β-plus γ-carotene, the remainder being torulin and torularhodin.

A striking effect of environmental conditions on pigment production has been observed, but these effects may vary greatly with the yeast strain or species. For instance, *Rhodotorula rubra* had essentially the same reddish color when grown at 25°C as at 5°C, but a particular strain of *Rh. glutinis* was salmon-pink when grown at 25°C and a dark yellow after growth at 5°C. Another species, *Rh. peneaus,* was canary-yellow at 25°C but cream-colored at the low temperature.

The amount of pigment formed is strongly depressed in some strains when grown in aerated cultures; in other strains aeration has little influence. Some oxygen is obviously required since not only are species of these genera strict aerobes, but colonies growing on a plate show a much higher pigment concentration at the surface than in the deeper layers. Finally, the carbon compound of a synthetic medium upon which these yeasts are grown affects the color and pigment composition of certain strains, whereas others are only slightly affected or not at all. Mutations affecting pigment synthesis have also been noted.

As a result of these considerations it is not surprising that many taxonomists feel that the property of a yeast to produce carotenoid pigments should carry very little weight in the differentiation of species and varieties and that even for generic definition this property has only limited value.

Not all pinkish colonies of yeast owe this color to carotenoid pigments. It has long been known that upon streaking of the yeast *Candida pulcherrima* some, or occasionally all, of the colonies assume a deep maroon-red color, which occasionally diffuses into the medium, forming a reddish halo around the growth. At the beginning of the century Beijerinck had already established that this pigment was insoluble in organic solvents (in contrast to the carotenoid pigments), was slightly soluble in water, but could be extracted with alkali and re-precipitated with acid. It is now known that the formation of this pigment, which has been named pulcherrimin, is dependent on the presence of iron in the medium. Pulcherrimin is a symmetrical macromolecule of high molecular weight, containing 12.7% iron in addition to carbon, hydrogen, oxygen, and nitrogen. Its unit structure may be regarded as the iron salt of pulcherriminic acid, a pyrazine derivative. Pulcherrimin is also produced by heavily sporulating species of *Fabospora, Hansenula,* and *Pichia,* and by some strains of *Saccharomyces* growing in biotin deficient media.

Little detailed knowledge is available on the dark pigments of the so-called "black yeasts," which are usually placed in the genus *Pullularia.* Usually, colonies are initially white. After a few days they go through a pinkish or greenish stage, finally becoming deep brown or jet black. The pigment appears to be related to the melanins and is insoluble in water and in the usual organic solvents.

Another group of metabolic by-products are capsular poly-saccharides (phosphomannans, starch-like compounds and various heteropolysaccharides), which are released into the medium by some species. For further details the reader is referred to the chapter on cytology and that on industrial uses of yeast.

VII / Nutrition and Growth

In this chapter we will describe the conditions under which yeasts are normally grown in the laboratory. This information applies to the vast majority of yeasts. Some mention will be made of yeasts with unusual growth requirements. The latter organisms have highly specialized habitats which often reflect their need for special growth factors.

The usual growth requirements of yeast include a carbon source, a source of organic or inorganic nitrogen, various minerals (including compounds furnishing trace elements), and lastly a mixture of vitamins.

Because of the close relation between the developmental history of yeast and the field of brewing, one of the oldest classical media used for the cultivation of yeast is malt extract or beer wort. This medium contains all of the above ingredients and can be used in liquid form or as a solid medium after the addition of agar. In some countries it is nowadays available in the convenient form of a spray-dried powder or syrup; these can simply be dissolved or diluted with water to a concentration of one to ten percent soluble solids, depending on what is desired. This medium is sometimes modified by the addition of some yeast extract or yeast autolysate, and peptone. Wickerham recommends the following medium for maintaining or storing yeasts.

.3% malt extract   1% glucose
.3% yeast extract   2% agar
.5% peptone

In general, yeast is not affected appreciably by changes in pH and nearly all species can grow within a wide range of pH values. In the authors' experience there are few, if any, yeasts that are inhibited by a pH value of 3.0, provided the acidification is done with hydrochloric or phosphoric acid. Certain organic acids, however, are inhibitory to the growth of yeasts. At the other end of the pH scale, yeasts readily grow at pH values of 7–8 and often even higher, but optimum growth is normally found somewhere in the range between pH 4.5 and 6.5.

Yeast autolysate is another commonly used complex medium; it contains all of the above-mentioned necessary growth requirements with the exception of a fermentable carbon source. The word "fermentable" is stressed here since many yeasts can grow to a greater or smaller extent at the expense of the available amino acids in yeast autolysate, but fermentation and gas production are not possible with amino acids. A boiling water extract of compressed baker's yeast, however, may contain some of the reserve sugar trehalose, which is fermentable by some yeasts. For this reason autolyzed yeast, in which these reserve sugars are destroyed, is preferred as a basal medium; the desired sugar can then be added for a particular fermentation test.

In many growth experiments use is made of synthetic media. An example of two widely used synthetic media, developed by Wickerham, is given in Table 1. These very useful

TABLE 1. Composition of chemically defined media for growing yeasts. Amounts are given per liter of distilled water.

	Yeast Nitrogen Base	Yeast Carbon Base
CARBON SOURCE	*grams*	*grams*
D-glucose	none[a]	10
NITROGEN SOURCE		
$(NH_4)_2SO_4$	5.0	none[b]
SALTS		
KH_2PO_4	1.0	1.0
$MgSO_4 \cdot 7H_2O$	0.5	0.5
NaCl	0.1	0.1
$CaCl_2 \cdot 2H_2O$	0.1	0.1
AMINO ACIDS	*milligrams*	*milligrams*
L-histidine $\cdot$ HCl $\cdot$ H_2O	10	1.0
DL-methionine	20	2.0
DL-tryptophan	20	2.0[c]
COMPOUNDS SUPPLYING TRACE ELEMENTS	*micrograms*	*micrograms*
H_3BO_3	500	500
$CuSO_4 \cdot 5H_2O$	40	40
KI	100	100
$FeCl_3 \cdot 6H_2O$	200	200
$MnSO_4 \cdot 1H_2O$	400	400
$Na_2MoO_4 \cdot 2H_2O$	200	200
$ZnSO_4 \cdot 7H_2O$	400	400
VITAMINS		
Biotin	2	2
Calcium pantothenate	400	400
Folic acid	2	2
Inositol	2000	2000
Niacin	400	400
Para-aminobenzoic acid	200	200
Pyridoxine $\cdot$ HCl	400	400
Riboflavin	200	200
Thiamine $\cdot$ HCl	400	400

[a] The desired carbon source must be added.

[b] The desired nitrogen source must be added.

[c] The nitrogen contained in these three amino acids is insufficient to support visible growth.

media are now sold commercially in prepared form. As will be noted, Yeast Nitrogen Base contains a number of trace elements, nine vitamins, trace amounts of amino acids to stimulate growth of certain fastidious yeasts, and the principal minerals: potassium phosphate, magnesium sulfate, sodium chloride, and calcium chloride. The nitrogen source is ammonium sulfate, which can be utilized by the vast majority of all yeasts known. The desired carbon source must be added, normally in a concentration of 0.5 to 1%. The carbon sources which can be utilized by yeast vary greatly with the species. Glucose is utilized by all yeasts, although it is not necessarily the most effective carbon source. Categories of carbon sources which various yeasts can assimilate include hexose sugars, di-, tri-, and polysaccharides, pentose sugars, methyl pentoses, sugar alcohols, organic acids, and some miscellaneous compounds. Use is made of the ability or inability of yeasts to assimilate various carbon compounds in the differentiation of species.

In Yeast Carbon Base medium, glucose is the carbon source but a source of nitrogen is lacking. This medium can be used to determine which nitrogen sources a yeast can use for growth. Categories include single amino acids, purine and pyrimidine bases, amines, urea, nitrate, nitrite, ammonia, and others. As was true for carbon sources, yeast species vary greatly in their ability to satisfy their nitrogen demand by the above sources, with the exception of ammonium ion which is suitable for practically all yeasts. Urea is also quite generally assimilated, but often rather weakly. The suitability of individual amino acids as a nitrogen source depends on the ability of the yeast to deaminate a particular amino acid and to incorporate the ammonia into other nitrogenous constituents of the cell. Normally, if a yeast can utilize nitrate it is also able to utilize nitrite as a nitrogen source. Nitrite, however, is often quite toxic, especially if used in too high a concentration. All species of the genus *Hansenula* can utilize nitrate and nitrite. Some species of *Debaryomyces* are known to utilize nitrite, but not nitrate; this may be attributed to the lack of an enzyme to reduce nitrate to nitrite.

Although nine vitamins are included in the synthetic media discussed above, yeasts vary widely in their requirements for vitamins. It would appear that biotin is the most commonly required vitamin and riboflavin the least. In fact, there is some doubt that riboflavin is required by any yeasts. Many free-living species (such as *Hansenula anomala*) grow vigorously in vitamin-free media and they synthesize all of the necessary vitamins themselves. Most species of *Saccharomyces* require one or more vitamins, although vitamin-independent strains of *Saccharomyces cerevisiae* are known to exist.

The statement that a yeast requires a particular vitamin is often qualified by stating that the requirement is an absolute one or a relative one. Yeast having an absolute requirement for a vitamin cannot grow in the absence of this nutrilite, irrespective of the time of incubation. A relative requirement indicates that the yeast can very slowly synthesize this particular growth factor, but will grow much more rapidly if it is supplied in the medium. Yeasts with absolute vitamin requirements are useful for vitamin assays of complex substrates. As an example, all of the apiculate yeasts belonging to *Kloeckera* or *Hanseniaspora* have an absolute requirement for pantothenic acid and for inositol. Like most lactose-fermenting yeasts, *Saccharomyces fragilis* has an absolute requirement for niacin. Some investigators have attempted a biochemical classification of yeast strains on the basis of individual vitamin requirements, and in some genera, such as *Rhodotorula,* some of the species appear to have characteristic vitamin needs. These studies need considerable expansion, however, before the usefulness of specific vitamin requirements in taxonomy is established. At present the main use of vitamins in taxonomy is to determine whether or not a yeast is able to propagate in a vitamin-free synthetic medium.

The optimal temperature of growth depends on the particular species with which we deal. There is no such thing as a common denominator, a temperature at which all yeasts will grow. We may say, however, that for nearly all purposes a temperature of 20–25°C is suitable for the growth of the vast majority. Many free-living yeasts are unable to grow at 30°C, and the use of an incubator at this temperature, therefore, is undesirable.

Two categories of yeast may form exceptions to this temperature range. There are a number of yeasts, typically associated with warm-blooded animals, which, in some cases, have a minimum growth temperature of 35°C, whereas other species have a minimum of 28°C. At the other extreme, yeasts have been isolated from arctic regions; often these barely grow at 20°C and their optimum temperature is somewhere near 15°C. In both of these examples there is a clear relationship between the habitats of the yeasts and their optimum temperature. Table 2 gives certain examples of growth ranges of yeast which the authors have determined in their laboratory. Obviously there are enormous variations in the range under which yeasts are able to grow. It is well to emphasize that maximal cell crops in the upper part of a given range are reached very rapidly. If no growth occurs after a few days we may conclude that the yeast is unable to grow at that particular temperature. At the lower part of a range the situation is quite different, since it may take one month or longer to reach maximal cell crops due to the very low rate of growth.

TABLE 2. Examples of growth ranges of several species of yeast. It may be well to emphasize that variations of several degees in minimum and maximum temperatures of growth are normal for different strains of the same species.

	0	10	20	30	40	50°C
Candida macedoniensis		●————————————————————●				
Debaryomyces hansenii		●——————————————●				
Nadsonia elongata		●————————————●				
Candida scottii		●—————————●				
Saccharomycopsis guttulata					●——●	
Candida slooffii				●————————●		
Saccharomyces mellis				●————————●		
Schizosaccharomyces octosporus			●————————●			
Pichia membranaefaciens		●————————————●				
Saccharomyces fragilis		●————————————————————●				
	0	10	20	30	40	50°C

The discussion above has dealt mainly with normal growth requirements in which the vast majority of yeasts would be included. A number of highly exacting species are known, however, which are those with unusual growth requirements. These will be dealt with briefly. Several species of yeast occur as harmless parasites in the intestinal tract of warm-blooded animals. One member of this group, *Saccharomycopsis guttulata*, is a large, budding yeast, occurring in the intestinal tract of rabbits (and of a few other rodents). It was first observed in that habitat in 1845, but, in spite of repeated attempts, it was not until approximately 1955 that the organism was successfully cultured on artificial media. In its natural habitat the yeast obtains its complex nutrient requirements from the food being digested in the stomach of the rabbit. It was observed that growth could not be sustained in malt extract, a fairly complex medium in itself. However, growth of this yeast is possible in media containing glucose and the filtrate of thoroughly autolyzed yeast. Growth also occurs in synthetic media, provided that certain protein hydrolysates are added. Suitable in this respect are Proteose Peptone and Trypticase (a pancreatic digest of casein). It has been possible to replace the complex protein hydrolysates with a mixture of 21 synthetic amino acids, but exactly which amino acids are required is not known at the present time. Other unusal aspects of *Saccharomycopsis guttulata* are a requirement for carbon dioxide in the atmosphere and a temperature range between 35 and 40°C. Certain other intestinal parasitic yeasts are known to be somewhat less fastidious in their growth requirements.

Other yeasts are found to be strongly osmophilic, indicating that they thrive best in high concentrations of sugar. Most of these yeasts, as exemplified by *Saccharomyces mellis* and *S. rouxii*, are found growing in honey and other media with high sugar content. It is nearly always possible to adapt these osmophilic yeasts to media with low sugar content by transferring them progressively on media with lower and lower sugar concentrations. Only rarely are osmophilic yeasts found which cannot be adapted to growth at low sugar concentrations. An example of an obligate osmophile is *Eremascus albus*, a yeast-like spoilage organism of foods with high osmotic pressure. This yeast requires a minimum of 40% sugar in media for it to grow properly.

The situation is somewhat different with salt. Several yeasts, especially species of the genus *Debaryomyces*, can grow slowly in nearly saturated solutions of sodium chloride, but they can be readily grown on ordinary media containing no sodium chloride at all. Such yeasts might be designated as osmoduric, indicating that they can withstand high levels of salt but do not require them. Similarly, yeasts isolated from sea water grow just as well on media without salt as in media containing 3–4% NaCl. Hence, yeasts behave differently from several halophilic bacterial species which require salt for growth.

The long-known species *Pityrosporum ovale*, which has its habitat on the scalp of humans and on the skin of certain animals, is known to require fats for growth. Fat is an absolute requirement and it was believed for many years that unsaturated fatty acids, in particular oleic acid, were the required growth factors. Recently, however, by the use of highly purified fatty acids, it was shown that *P. ovale* does not grow in a basal medium supplemented with pure oleic acid. The growth requirements can be satisfied, instead, by myristic acid or by palmitic acid. However, oleate increases the crop of organisms in media containing limited concentrations of myristate or palmitate.

Other unusual growth requirements are found among species of the genus *Brettanomyces*. These very slow growing yeasts are now known to require unusually high concentrations of thiamine in the medium, up to 10,000 μg per liter, nearly 25 times as much as is required by most yeasts.

Although not a growth requirement, use is often made of

calcium carbonate as a buffer in the medium to protect those yeasts which produce large amounts of acetic acid and other organic acids. Species of *Brettanomyces* are especially short-lived, because the acetic acid produced on solid media during aerobic growth tends to kill off the cells very rapidly. Incorporation of 0.5 to 1% calcium carbonate in the medium protects these cultures for an appreciable period against the toxic effects of acetic acid.

VIII / *Ecology*

The field of yeast ecology is concerned with the manner in which yeasts live and propagate in nature, where specific organisms can be found, and, conversely, what the yeast population is in or on substrates which can support their growth. It is also concerned with the interaction between yeasts and other groups of microorganisms — fungi, bacteria, and protozoa — as well as the higher forms of life, ranging from insects to warm-blooded animals on the one hand and from algae to the vascular plants on the other. Most yeasts live a saprophytic form of life, indicating that they grow on dead organic substrates, but parasitic types are also known, and these depend largely on a living host to supply the necessary nutrients. Interaction between yeasts and other groups of microorganisms, living side by side on a particular substrate, is not necessarily limited to competition for a share of the available nutrients, although it is certainly an important factor. Several forms of interaction may be cited.

1. One organism may make available components of a substrate which would otherwise be unavailable to a second organism. For example, no yeasts are known which can grow on cellulose or xylan. Many molds and bacteria, however, can attack these polymers, usually by hydrolysis with extracellular enzymes, and yeasts can profit from this action by utilizing a

portion of the breakdown products. In this connection we have observed that nearly all yeasts occurring in association with trees and bark beetles can utilize cellobiose and D-xylose as single carbon sources. A similar example could be given of starch breakdown by molds, followed by yeast development.

2. Some actinomycetes produce antibiotics which inhibit, in extremely low concentrations, the growth of certain fungi and yeasts. Although conditions in industry have been adjusted to obtain very high yields of these compounds, they undoubtedly are also produced in natural substrates, and in concentrations sufficient to affect the composition of the yeast population. Considerable variation in sensitivity of yeasts to these antibiotics has been demonstrated. Examples are cycloheximide (actidione) and the polyene class of antibiotics, both produced by species of *Streptomyces*.

3. Major metabolic products of bacteria can also inhibit yeast growth or kill cells already present. Acetic acid, produced by vinegar bacteria from alcohol formed by yeasts, is an example. Many yeasts are very sensitive to acetic acid in the undissociated form, although exceptions are known (see Chapter IX).

4. Some bacterial metabolic products of uncertain nature have been reported to inhibit yeast growth; their action does not appear to be very specific. Examples are species of several common genera of soil bacteria, a pseudomonad of marine origin, and a particular strain of *Acetobacter mesoxidans*. The antagonistic action of the last organism does not appear to be caused by acetic acid.

5. Ingestion of yeasts by insects, protozoa, and other animals occurs commonly. Such organisms consume the yeasts as food.

We have observed on a few occasions the rather tenacious association of protozoa in cultures of apiculate yeasts.

Since yeasts cannot be recognized with the naked eye (even one million baker's yeast cells suspended in a liter of water do not create a visible turbidity), information on the distribution of yeasts in nature must depend on culturing of substrates suspected of harboring yeasts. Even microscopic observation of natural substrates will reveal the presence of yeasts only if they are present in very large numbers. Let us take the above example again, where 10^6 cells were suspended in a liter of water. If a droplet of this suspension is placed on a microscope slide and covered with a coverslip, the observer would have great difficulty in finding a single cell in the preparation, unless aided by luck.

It is well to describe briefly the methods used in the enumeration of the different species of yeasts which are present in a natural substrate, because the methods strongly influence the results, and a number of pitfalls in methodology will soon become apparent. In spite of shortcomings, the preferred procedure is to plate the material on an agar medium which is likely to support the growth of the yeasts present. A limitation of this technique becomes apparent immediately. An average Petri dish cannot support more than approximately 500 separate colonies. If a greater number of cells is inoculated the resultant colonies tend to grow together. This creates difficulties, since we have to depend primarily on the appearance of colonies to make an estimate of the various types or species which develop. This, then, implies that if the population contains minority types — let us say less than one in 500, or 0.2% — it is unlikely that these types would appear on the plate. Since

Petri dishes, inoculated with natural substrates, often contain less than 500 colonies — sometimes only a dozen or so — it is evident that minority types could easily be overlooked. Yet it is the only method we have that can give a reasonable estimate of the yeasts which are found in natural substrates.

Many studies in the past have made use of so-called enrichment cultures in liquid media. In this procedure, a small amount of the substrate is inoculated into a liquid culture and allowed to grow for several days until the presence of yeasts becomes apparent visually, or upon microscopic inspection. This material is then plated and colonies are isolated. The weakness of this procedure is that in the artificial medium in which the substrate was inoculated, minority types could easily outgrow majority types, if the former found life in the artificial medium more advantageous. Thus, a completely erroneous picture would be obtained of the actual yeasts present in the material under study. The following is a simple example: suppose there are in a sample of flower nectar 1000 organisms belonging to *Cryptococcus* and a single yeast cell belonging to *Saccharomyces*. If this material is inoculated into a medium containing glucose and yeast autolysate and left until growth is apparent, the population in all likelihood would have a ratio of *Saccharomyces* : *Cryptococcus* of many thousands to one. Thus, upon plating and isolation, the impression would be gained that *Saccharomyces* was the predominant type or even the only species in the original substrate.

On solid media one of the problems which must be overcome is competition by bacteria and molds. As explained in Chapter VII, yeasts can withstand low pH values unusually well and adjustment of ordinary nutrient media to a pH between 3.5 and 3.8 is ordinarily sufficient to inhibit the growth of the vast majority of competing bacteria. Another approach is to incorporate in the medium one or more broad-spectrum bacterial antibiotics, which do not affect yeasts.

The control of molds is more difficult, since yeasts are also fungi and thus closely related. They frequently respond in the same way to inhibitory conditions. The most troublesome fungi are those which have a strongly spreading type of growth, as species of *Mucor* or *Rhizopus*. Fortunately, only a limited number of natural substrates (for example, soil samples and spoiled fruits) contain these fungi in abundance. In each survey, preliminary experiments should be conducted to determine the extent to which fungal growth may be expected to interfere with the isolation of yeasts. Some antifungal agents have been used with a fair degree of success. Propionic acid is most effective at low pH values, but under certain conditions it also inhibits the growth of yeasts. The best approach is to select a borderline concentration which reduces the rate of growth of the molds and yet allows the yeasts to grow. Other investigators have used dilute dye solutions (for example, 0.003% rose bengal) or 1% ox gall incorporated in potato extract glucose agar. The last two agents seem to work best in media which are not too rich in nutrients and therefore do not permit such a rapid growth of the fungi. Lastly, some workers have used shaken cultures in which the fungal spores germinate and form small mycelial balls, preventing the formation of conidia or spores. After a limited amount of growth, the fungal mycelium can be filtered off over sterilized glass wool and the yeasts in the filtrates can be determined by conventional means. This method, however, has the inherent disadvantage of all enrichment techniques.

The media for isolating yeasts are ordinarily 5% malt extract agar, Wickerham's maintenance agar (see Chapter VII), or a medium containing 0.5% powdered yeast autolysate plus 5% glucose. When bacteria are a problem, the pH is adjusted to 3.7 with hydrochloric acid. Since agar breaks down when autoclaved at such a low pH, a previously determined amount of 1N HCl is added aseptically to the medium after autoclaving and before pouring it into the Petri dishes. Special conditions as to additional growth factors, temperature of incubation, substrate concentration, and other details have been discussed in Chapter VII. In general, it is wise to simulate, more or less, the environmental conditions under which the yeast is found in its natural habitat.

Before inoculating the plates, consideration should be given to possible pretreatment of the sample and to the amount of inoculum. It is best for substrates which are in a desiccated condition to be rehydrated in a small amount of sterile water or in an atmosphere saturated with moisture, allowing suffi-cient time for proper rehydration. Insect or plant material may require dissection to avoid plating parts which may con-tain accidental impurities or contaminants. As an example, a number of studies have been made on the food intake of insects which feed on certain substrates that contain yeasts. In order to avoid isolating yeasts which accidentally adhere to the legs, body, and wings of these insects, procedures have been devel-oped for removing the intestinal tract or the crop, and specif-ically plating these organs on agar plates. It becomes even more difficult if the study involves yeasts which have their habitat inside certain specialized cells of the insect body — for example, mycetomal tissue or the epithelial layer of certain portions in the intestinal canal. The isolation of yeasts from such tissues requires considerable skill and experience.

Another problem, encountered in the study of yeasts which have been ingested by insects, is the rapidity with which these microorganisms are digested. We have shown that drosophila flies, which were permitted to feed on baker's yeast, contained in their crops an average of 150,000 yeast cells per individual after feeding. After 24 hours at room temperature this number had dropped to 65, and after 48 hours of starvation the yeast count was zero. The yeast content in an insect, therefore, depends strongly on the time of last feeding in relation to the time of dissection. For this reason insects which are captured for a study of their microflora should be dissected as rapidly as possible; or they should be refrigerated to temperatures close to O°C, where the rate of digestion is greatly reduced.

The amount of inoculum can sometimes be estimated after microscopic inspection of the material to be plated. If the yeast population is low in numbers, however, samples of various size should be tried and, in time, experience will show the proper amount of inoculum to obtain a number of colonies not exceeding 300-500 per petri dish.

The only way to correlate the identity of the colonies appearing on plates with the original population in the sample is to estimate as accurately as possible the number of different types of yeast present. Since a great deal of work is involved in the identification of individual yeast isolates, it is obviously impossible to identify all colonies. Fortunately, many species exhibit pronounced or subtle differences in gross morphology of the colonies, and groups or categories can be recognized with some experience. Features to which particular attention is paid are variations in color, surface topography, degree of glossiness, texture (varying from very slimy, through pasty, to hard and tough), form or cross section of a colony, its degree of spreading or colony diameter, and, finally, the periphery, or border, which may show characteristic markings or hyphal development in the form of a feathery or ciliate edge. Often the colony morphology is characteristic of certain genera or species, although the composition of the media and even the substitution of agar by gelatin may exert a profound influence. Some of these features are illustrated in Fig.15. For example, on malt agar, red, mucous colonies usually represent species of the genus *Rhodotorula;* dull, powdery, red colonies the genus *Sporobolomyces;* glossy, mucous, colorless colonies could belong to either the genus *Cryptococcus* or *Lipomyces.* Colonies which are cone-shaped with gently sloping sides, and have a silky appearance, often are members of the genus *Hanseniaspora;* and colonies with an extensive development of hyphal growth at the periphery, and which gradually change color from white to brown or black, are members of the genus *Pullularia.*

It must be kept in mind that this method of selecting colonies has its limitations, since some closely related organisms possess almost identical colony morphology. Conversely, yeasts with different colony morphology may represent the same species, since, especially in haploid yeasts, mutations are not infrequent. These often show up in a somewhat different colony morphology, or in the form of sectors.

Valuable additional information can be gathered by taking small samples of various colonies and making microscopic observations of cell morphology, vegetative reproduction, and striking cytological features. Occasionally, even ascospore formation can be observed in the primary colonies of the isolation plate. Finally, one or two representative types of each kind of colony are brought in pure culture by the usual streaking techniques. Although isolations are usually made after 2–4 days of growth, plates should not be discarded at this time, since very slow-growing colonies may not appear until after one or two weeks. Some yeasts are naturally very slow growers, while others grow slowly because their cells may be in a weakened condition in the natural substrate. Some are present as spores which may require some time for germination.

In Chapter IV it was pointed out that heterothallic yeasts are found in nature, which means that two mating types of such yeasts occur separately in natural substrates. If such a yeast is isolated by the usual purification steps, the culture generally represents the offspring of a single haploid cell, and thus would not be expected to produce ascospores unless it is mixed with cells of the opposite mating type. Clues as to the occurrence of natural mating types can be obtained in isolation material by inspecting samples where the growth is dense and many colonies are intermixed. Since mating types often, although not always, occur in the same material, such a sample may show conjugation tubes or zygotes. If the isolated pure cultures are negative in this respect, such observations would suggest that one is dealing with a haploid, heterothallic species. Even if conjugation is not seen in the impure material, it is worthwhile to pursue testing for heterothallism in nonsporogenous isolates.

The procedures outlined above present the general principles involved in obtaining an insight into the population distribution of yeasts occurring in natural substrates. Occasionally, however, information may be desired as to the occurrence of specific yeasts in materials which may contain a considerable excess of other species. For the quantitative enumeration of such specific yeasts it is sometimes possible to use selective media and incubation conditions suitable for the growth of one or very few species, thus preventing growth of the others. The

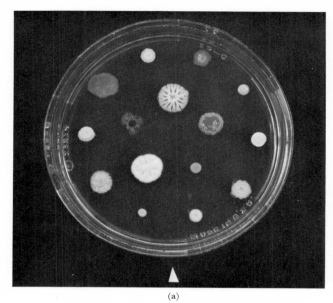

(a)

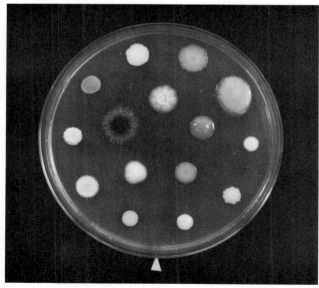

(b)

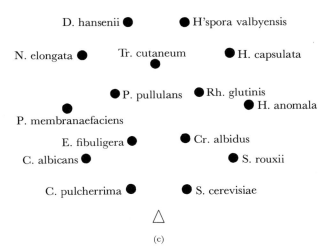

D. hansenii ● ● H'spora valbyensis

N. elongata ● Tr. cutaneum ● H. capsulata
●

● P. pullulans ● Rh. glutinis
● ● H. anomala
P. membranaefaciens

E. fibuligera ● ● Cr. albidus
C. albicans ● ● S. rouxii

C. pulcherrima ● ● S. cerevisiae

△

(c)

Fig. 15. Colonies of 15 selected yeast cultures grown for eight days at 18°C in 9-cm Petri dishes containing 5% malt gelatin (a), and for comparison 5% malt agar (b). The chart (c) is a key to the position of the culture.

spectrum of carbon and nitrogen sources which yeasts can utilize has been discussed in Chapter VII, and application of these principles can be made in the isolation of certain yeasts from nature. A few examples will illustrate this approach.

Yeasts which can utilize melibiose as a single carbon source are not as common as yeasts which are unable to use this disaccharide. By incorporating melibiose into Yeast Nitrogen Base (see p. 85), the selective condition is created which will allow melibiose-utilizing yeasts to develop, whereas others are unable to grow on this medium. In this way it is possible to detect and count *Saccharomyces carlsbergensis* cells (a melibiose-positive beer yeast) in a population of *S. cerevisiae*, a melibiose-negative brewer's yeast. Similar variations can be made with other carbon sources. In the same way, media can be prepared in which glucose is the carbon source (Yeast Carbon Base, p. 85) and the nitrogen source is varied. If nitrate is supplied, material streaked on this medium will produce colonies only if the yeast in question can utilize nitrate. This technique has been useful in the detection of small numbers of *Candida utilis* contaminants in baker's yeast plants. *Candida utilis* is nitrate-positive and baker's yeast is nitrate-negative. Other nitrogen sources which have been suggested for differentiation include nitrite, ethylamine, L-lysine, and creatine.

Sometimes it is advantageous to use a combination of two or more selective conditions to favor a particular yeast. A case in point is the isolation of *Brettanomyces* species from spoiled wines, in which such yeasts occasionally occur, but from which they are very difficult to isolate. Van der Walt and co-workers have found that *Brettanomyces* species can be isolated with a much greater degree of success if the medium is fortified with thiamine to a concentration of 10,000 μg per liter. *Brettanomyces* species require unusually high concentrations of this vitamin. In addition, the medium is supplied with 100 µg per liter of the fungal antibiotic cycloheximide (actidione), to which *Brettanomyces* is very resistant. Wine yeasts are completely inhibited by as little as a few parts per million of this compound. These two selective conditions have made it possible to isolate cultures of the very slowly growing *Brettanomyces* yeasts from populations containing a vast majority of wine yeasts.

Another example relates to the isolation of strains of *Saccharomyces fragilis* from natural sources. In this case we are dealing with a thermoduric, lactose-fermenting species, and thus it is helpful to use media containing lactose as the carbon source and to incubate the plates at 45°C, since *S. fragilis* is one of the few yeasts that grow well at this relatively high temperature. Another hypothetical combination of conditions could be the following: vitamin-free synthetic medium, nitrate as the nitrogen source, i-erythritol as the carbon source, incubation at 0°C. A combination of these selective conditions certainly would eliminate the vast majority of possible competitors. Variations can also be made in the sugar or salt content of the medium, the oxygen and CO_2 concentration of the atmosphere of incubation, and others. Establishment of such selective conditions, of course, presupposes an adequate knowledge of the metabolic peculiarities of a particular yeast.

Now the question must be considered as to what to select as inoculum, if one should wish to isolate a certain species from nature. Experience has shown that yeasts are not as ubiquitous as are many bacteria. Yeasts generally have a more specific habitat and the chance of isolating them, therefore, increases considerably by employing the proper substrate in isolation attempts. As indicated earlier, knowledge of the distribution of yeasts in nature has been gathered from numerous surveys made by various workers. Results from these surveys indicate that some substrates are highly selective and contain only a few species of yeast (or sometimes only a single species), whereas others are much less exclusive and contain rather a wide variety. Even in the latter, predominant types are usually found.

We shall now describe briefly certain habitats and hosts which have been studied in considerable detail. These surveys, done by many different investigators, have yielded some general conclusions as to the predominant yeast florae occurring in them. This will at the same time give the reader some information as to where yeasts are generally found in nature. Surprisingly, yeasts occur almost everywhere, but in vastly different population densities and with great selectivity in habitat. We shall stress in this chapter primarily their natural habitats and in Chapter IX discuss more specifically how yeasts can occur as spoilage organisms in foods of various compositions.

YEASTS ASSOCIATED WITH PLANTS

1. *Leaves*. The external surface of the leaf as an environment for microorganisms has been termed the phyllosphere. The possibility of its being a habitat for yeasts and other microorganisms has been recognized only in recent years. Ruinen has shown that healthy leaves of tropical plants normally carry a rich flora of nitrogen-fixing bacteria. As leaves are also the site of photosynthesis of the plant, it is not surprising that yeasts occur in the phyllosphere, sometimes in large numbers. Leaves of elm trees and other species often

exude a sugary fluid (not related to the presence of aphids) which can supply the necessary carbon source for yeast growth. However, even minute amounts of sugar, insufficient to be evident to the naked eye, could support a considerable number of yeast cells. The work of Ruinen in the tropics and that of di Menna on pasture grasses in New Zealand has shown that only a limited number of species were present and that the great majority belonged to the asporogenous, nonfermentative genera *Cryptococcus* and *Rhodotorula*. Also, *Pullularia* species (the black yeasts) were found regularly. In addition to species belonging to the last three genera, we have found fermentative yeasts, such as *Saccharomyces rosei, S. pretoriensis,* and *S. veronae,* in the sugary exudate of elm leaves in California. Species of *Sporobolomyces* appear commonly on the leaves and grains of cereal grasses.

The yeast flora of leaves shows seasonal variation in numbers. It ranges between 3×10^4 and 3×10^6 per gram of pasture plant leaves during most of the year, with increases to 10^8 per gram in late summer, when 90% of the population consists of red-pigmented species. Possibly, these red, carotenoid-containing species are better protected against sunlight than nonpigmented species. Another factor of possible significance is the presence of a slimy capsule in nearly all species obtained from leaves.

2. *Flowers.* A considerable amount of work has been done on the yeast flora of flowers. It would seem reasonable that flowers harbor yeasts, since the nectar found at the base of the corolla of many species offers sugar upon which yeast can grow. Inoculation and transfer from flower to flower is made possible by bees responsible for pollination, by wasps, butterflies, and many other insects which feed on flower nectar.

Yet most investigators have found that an appreciable percentage of flower samples (usually well over 50%) contain either no yeasts or at most very few cells. On the other hand, counts of over one million yeasts per large flower, or per cluster of small flowers, have also been reported. Low counts or absence of yeasts could be caused by the very short life span of some flowers, absence of insect pollination, absence of nectar glands, and sampling too soon after a flower opens. Seasonal variations in yeast population also play a significant role, the numbers being highest in mid-summer.

The yeasts reported from flowers form a fairly well-defined group. Strange as it may seem, most of the yeasts are strictly oxidative, the fermentative types forming a small minority. The black yeasts, belonging to the genus *Pullularia*, are perhaps most common, often comprising well over half of the total number of cells present in a sample. Species of *Cryptococcus, Rhodotorula,* and *Sporobolomyces* are next in abundance, to be followed by species of *Candida* and *Torulopsis*. As a rule very few sporulating yeasts are isolated, all of the above genera representing asporogenous organisms.

Among the species of *Candida,* two are particularly worth mentioning, *C. reukaufii* and the closely related *C. pulcherrima.* The first species was once known as *Anthomyces reukaufii* and later as *Nectaromyces reukaufii,* both names referring to their origin in flowers. In our laboratory we have isolated this yeast repeatedly from the flowers of the shrub *Teucrium fruticans* in California. This yeast, as it grows in the nectar of flowers, has a very characteristic thallus in the form of large cells arranged in an airplane-like shape (Fig. 16). *C. pulcherrima* can be isolated often from flowers as well as fruits, and on the latter they may originate from the blossoms. According to Wicker-

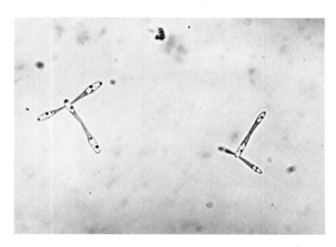

Fig. 16. Cells of *Candida reukaufii*, photographed directly in a droplet of nectar squeezed from flowers of the shrub *Teucrium fructicans*. Note the characteristic airplane shape resulting from the aggregation of three cells.

ham, *C. pulcherrima* and *C. reukaufii* belong in yet another genus, for which he has recently proposed the name *Chlamydozyma*.

3. *Tree exudates.* A wide variety of tree species all over the world shows the phenomenon of fluxing, the flowing of tree sap from a wound. The cause of this condition has been ascribed to injuries due to boring insects or frost cracks, in conjunction with bacterial infection of the wound. Tree fluxes normally persist year after year and do not appear to damage a tree appreciably, if at all. The flowing sap becomes heavily infected with bacteria and yeasts, but molds are relatively scarce. In addition, many insects find tree exudates attractive for oviposition, and larvae develop in them. The tree sap usually assumes a thick, slimy consistency (probably due to microbial polysaccharide formation) and for this reason it is often referred to as a "slime flux."

Extensive studies have been made of the yeast flora in slime fluxes, and some yeasts have their exclusive natural habitat in them. Species of *Nadsonia* have been found exclusively in fluxes of deciduous trees (mainly birch and beech) in areas with a cool to temperate climate (*Nadsonia* species do not grow above 25°C). Species of *Endomyces, Endomycopsis,* and *Pichia* have a similar habitat. In our experience one of the most common species in slime fluxes of broad-leaf trees is *Pichia pastoris,* a yeast first isolated by Guilliermond in 1919 from the exudate of a chestnut tree in France. In addition, there are a number of other species of *Pichia* and of the related genus *Hansenula,* which have habitats closely dependent on deciduous trees. Examples are *Pichia fluxuum, Hansenula angusta, H. mrakii,* and others. Species of *Prototheca,* a genus representing unicellular algae devoid of chlorophyll, are also very common in slime fluxes and should not be confused with yeast (see Chapter XI).

A few examples of species of other genera may be listed. *Saccharomyces kluyveri* is the only species of its genus which has been isolated almost exclusively from slime fluxes of deciduous trees. *Schizosaccharomyces versatilis* occurs regularly in exudates of deciduous oaks in Japan and occasionally in so-called "pine honey." *Saccharomycodes ludwigii* appears to occur mainly in deciduous trees in Europe.

It seems very likely that yeasts are introduced to slime fluxes by visiting insects. Once a yeast population is established, it usually carries only a few species and its population is quite constant. We have followed the yeast population of a particular flux of an elm tree throughout an entire year. The yeast flora was approximately constant, both qualitatively and quantitatively, consisting mainly of *Pichia pastoris, Trichosporon penicillatum,* and *Prototheca moriformis.* Apparently these three species have established a stable equilibrium between themselves and their natural environment. Other species, sporadically introduced by certain vectors, cannot maintain themselves in this particular habitat.

4. *Plant pathogenic yeasts.* Some yeasts are recognized as plant pathogens, but their pathogenicity is of a mild form as compared to that of phytopathogenic bacteria and higher fungi. For the purpose of this discussion we shall exclude yeasts which cause an active fermentative spoilage of soft-ripe fruits, since the yeast action is as a rule of a secondary nature after the fruit has been damaged in some way.

Yeasts responsible for plant diseases are primarily members of the genera *Nematospora* and *Ashbya,* the latter a yeast-like organism. Species of both genera have characteristic needle-shaped ascospores. The two best recognized species, *Nemato-*

spora coryli and *Ashbya gossypii,* have been reported in a number of host plants and almost exclusively from subtropical and tropical areas. Typical examples of host plants include cotton (the internal boll disease), lima beans and other legumes (yeast spot), coffee berries (coffee bean disease), tomatoes, pecans and hazelnuts, and citrus fruit. The condition in citrus fruit is called *inspissosis* and causes a local drying-out and collapse of the juice sacs and a wrinkling of the rind due to the growth of the yeast. The cotton boll disease is of considerable economic importance. The growth of the yeasts in immature, unopened bolls leads to a staining of the lint. The evidence points to hemipterous insects—bugs in particular—as the carriers or vectors of the diseases. A fungal disease transmitted in this way is referred to as *stigmatomycosis.*

YEASTS ASSOCIATED WITH ANIMALS

Nearly all of the information available on yeast-animal relationships pertains to various warm-blooded species (chiefly herbivorous mammals) and insects. We shall limit our discussion mainly to these two categories of animals.

1. *Warm-blooded animals.* Differentiation should be made between yeasts which form part of the normal intestinal flora and those responsible for certain pathological conditions. In surveying the yeasts occurring in the alimentary tract, information has been derived from fecal matter as well as direct sampling of the intestinal or stomach contents. These studies have shown that about half of the samples obtained from horses and cattle contained yeast. Swine have a high incidence of yeasts, close to 90%, which is due to the very regular occurrence of *Candida slooffii* in these animals. Similarly, rabbits have a very high incidence of yeasts, nearly always represented

by a single species, *Saccharomycopsis guttulata;* a number of small rodents, such as mice and rats, regularly carry *Torulopsis pintolopesii* and *Candida bovina.* A sexual stage has been discovered for the last species, which is called *Saccharomyces tellustris.* On the other hand, sheep and goats usually have a very low incidence of yeasts in their intestinal tract.

All of the yeasts mentioned above may be considered as obligate parasites of their particular hosts, since they grow poorly or not at all at room temperature or below, they have unusually stringent growth requirements, and have not—or very rarely—been isolated from natural substrates outside of the host. A number of other species may be considered as facultative parasites of warm-blooded animals, *i.e.* yeasts which are regularly isolated from sources outside the animal body, but which, due to their ability to grow at 37°C, can also multiply in the intestinal tract. Examples of such yeasts are *Candida krusei, C. tropicalis, C. parapsilosis,* and *Trichosporon cutaneum.*

Finally, a large number of miscellaneous yeasts have been isolated sporadically from intestinal contents or dung, which may be considered as incidental passers-by or transients, having been ingested with a particular food. Many of these species cannot grow at 37°C and may even be killed at that temperature. However, even if a yeast has the ability to grow at body temperatures, it may be unable to grow in the intestinal tract for various reasons, such as anaerobiosis and pH conditions.

Nonpathogenic yeasts also occur on the skin of animals and humans. Such organisms usually originate from various external sources with which the skin may come into contact. Species of *Pityrosporum* deserve special mention because of their frequent occurrence on the scalp of humans and on the skin of animals. *Pityrosporum* is often associated with dandruff, but not necessarily the cause of it. *P. ovale* (from human scalp) requires lipids for growth (see Chapter VII), and *P. canis* (from dogs) can grow without fat but is stimulated by its presence.

In the vast field of medical mycology yeasts play a relatively minor role, although in some instances yeast infections have caused serious illness and even death.

We shall limit our discussion to the true yeasts and merely mention that a number of medical fungi assume a yeast phase in the body of the host, whereas in culture they are typical fungi. As examples may be listed *Histoplasma capsulatum* (the cause of histoplasmosis) and *Blastomyces dermatitidis* (the cause of North American blastomycosis).

Yeasts which can, under certain circumstances, be responsible for infections include *Candida albicans, C. stellatoidea, C. tropicalis, C. parapsilosis, Torulopsis glabrata,* and *Cryptococcus neoformans.* With the possible exception of the last species, these yeasts must be considered as opportunists; they may cause pathologic conditions in susceptible individuals, often those in poor nutritional status. *Candida albicans,* which causes various forms of candidiasis or moniliasis of the skin, and particularly of mucous membranes (thrush), is quantitatively the most common pathogenic yeast. Surveys of a great number of animals have shown, however, that man, fowls, and hedgehogs are very common carriers of this yeast, apparently without ill effects. Only in cases of diabetes in man, debilitating disease, pregnancy, and especially upon treatment of patients with broad spectrum antibiotics (when the balancing bacterial flora is destroyed), is the disease likely to become apparent and even systemic. Other species of *Candida* are encountered more rarely as aetiologic agents for diseases, although they may accompany infections by certain fungi. *Torulopsis glabrata* has been isolated with some degree of frequency from infections of the urinary tract.

Cryptococcosis (torulosis), a disease caused by *Cryptococcus neoformans,* occurs relatively rarely, but proven cases are often dramatic and fatal. The yeast infection, at first entailing skin lesions, becomes systemic and involves the central nervous system, often causing a chronic meningitis, ending in death. The most important reservoir of this yeast in the animal world is believed to be pigeons, in whose droppings and nests the yeast has been repeatedly demonstrated by Emmons and others. Interestingly, *Cr. neoformans* was recently found in 9 out of 20 samples of slime flux from mesquite, a desert plant occurring in the Southwest of the United States.

2. *Insects.* Since insects are probably the most important vectors in the distribution of yeasts in nature, their relationship to yeast is particularly important. The frequent association of yeasts with insects is undoubtedly a result of the nutritional importance of microorganisms in the life cycle of many species of this very large class of animals.

A good illustration is found in members of the genus *Drosophila.* Many of its 600 or more described species feed on a variety of substrates which contain yeasts that are able to carry out an alcoholic fermentation. A number of extensive surveys have shown the regular presence of yeasts in the crop or in the intestinal tract of both the domestic fruit fly, *D. melanogaster,* and of a number of wild species. As was pointed out earlier in this chapter, the yeasts are actually digested; for this reason the number of yeast cells per fly depends on the available food supply and on the time between the last feeding and dissection of the insect.

The feeding of *Drosophila* on moist fermenting fruit is well known, and breeding is commonly done in the same substrate by *D. melanogaster*. Thus, in fruit orchards, in tomato fields, and near dumps where fruit residue is discarded, the food supply is not limiting and this species may develop into astronomical numbers. The most common yeasts found in the crops of *D. melanogaster* are the apiculate yeasts *Hanseniaspora* and *Kloeckera,* and also *Pichia kluyveri, Candida krusei,* and *Torulopsis stellata.*

The situation is quite different with wild species, which apparently are not tempted to utilize food which is easily but temporarily available. Their populations fluctuate much less and their biomass in a given area must be a function of the availability of a steady food supply. The yeasts which are common in the crops of wild species of *Drosophila* are *Saccharomyces veronae, S. montanus, S. cerevisiae* var. *tetrasporus, S. drosophilarum,* and *Hansenula angusta.* In spite of an extensive search for substrates containing these yeasts, the results have been largely negative. Some of the areas studied are extremely arid, where substrates with enough surface moisture to permit feeding are very scarce, or very small and ephemeral. One source of yeasts in the forests of the Sierra Nevada of California (where most of our studies were conducted) is the exudates of oaks and firs. Apparently, this source is not attractive as a source of food for adult flies, although some species use these slime fluxes for breeding purposes. The fundamentally different yeast florae in the crops of adult flies and in these fluxes is the basis of this conclusion.

In the areas under discussion there is yet another source of yeasts, which again is very different from the flora found in adult drosophila flies and in slime fluxes. These are the yeasts which are abundantly associated with bark beetles that attack coniferous trees.

The two genera of bark beetles which are commonly found in pine trees are *Ips* and *Dendroctonus,* whereas beetles of the genus *Scolytus* more commonly attack true firs (*Abies*) and Douglas firs (*Pseudotsuga*). The larval galleries of these insects are made in the phloem of the tree and result in rapid death of the host. A new crop of adults originating from these larvae then emerges through the bark and, after some flight, select another susceptible tree. After boring through the bark they oviposit and the cycle starts anew. Yeasts are found in large numbers in the galleries made by larvae and adults, in spite of the presence of oleoresins in the wood. Perhaps these chemicals have a selective action, since the yeast flora is very specific and consists mainly of weakly fermentative or oxidative types. *Hansenula capsulata* and *Candida silvicola* (the perfect stage of which is *Hansenula holstii*) are abundant in all species of pine trees; *Pichia pini* occurs in all except *Pinus jeffreyi*. Possibly the high concentration of n-heptane in the turpentine of this pine might have a selective inhibitory action on *Pichia pini*. Other pines lack this constituent.

In contrast, *Scolytus* beetles in firs usually contain nearly pure cultures of an entirely different yeast, *Pichia scolyti* (syn. *Endomycopsis scolyti*). Although this heterothallic yeast is occasionally found in association with *Ips* and *Dendroctonus*, species of *Scolytus* must be considered as its true host.

These examples clearly demonstrate the highly specific nature of the yeasts associated with certain insects which have their habitat in the same restricted area. Although it is still not known where wild, adult drosophila flies obtain their food in nature, these small insects nevertheless are extremely useful in surveying, at least in part, the yeast flora in unexplored areas. Drosophila flies have a world-wide distribution, and techniques have been developed to capture these insects after attracting them to a sterilized bait.

One final illustration of a characteristic association between an insect and a yeast might be cited — that involving the tiny fig wasp *Blastophaga psenes*. A brief explanation of its life cycle is necessary. The fig is a syconium, that is, a hollow receptacle lined with flowers. It contains an opening, or eye, more or less covered by scales, through which certain small insects may pass. The normal habitat of the fig wasp is the caprifig, an inedible variety, which produces three successive crops each year. Only the spring crop (profichi) produces both pollen and pistillate flowers. The fig wasp, which lives inside the fig, carries pollen from the profichi crop to the subsequent crop so that seeds are formed. The insect passes from one crop to the next until the cycle repeats itself. We have found an interesting microflora, quite constantly associated with the fig wasp, consisting of one species of bacterium, *Serratia plymuthica*, and a single species of yeast, which has been named *Candida guilliermondii* var. *carpophila*. Presumably these two microorganisms are useful to the fig wasp, either nutritionally or otherwise. It would lead too far to discuss the fascinating life cycle of the fig wasp in greater detail and to point out how it is used in the commercial production of edible figs. For further information the reader is referred to Condit's book, *The Fig*.

Brief mention should be made of a number of highly specific associations between yeasts and certain specialized tissues in the intestinal tract of insects, where these yeasts have established themselves as harmless *intracellular* parasites. Some of these yeasts have been obtained in pure culture, but others have been seen only in their natural habitat and have resisted efforts to isolate them.

The few examples cited, in relation to the enormous number of insect genera known, leads one to believe that the study of yeast-insect relationships has barely been initiated. The interesting specific associations so far discovered promise many additional fascinating habitats in other groups of insects.

Other forms of animal life. Outside of the areas of warm-blooded animals and insects, relatively little work has been done with regard to yeast habitats. This again points to fruitful areas of research, both from the standpoint of yeast ecology and from the point of view of the related animal species. The finding of *Metschnikowia* species as pathogens of *Daphnia magna* (a fresh water crustacean) and *Artemia salina* (the brine shrimp), and other associations, points in this direction.

YEASTS IN SOILS

The soil, in most cases, should be considered more as a reservoir than as a habitat where yeasts can multiply freely. Since the soil receives plant, fungal (mushroom), and animal residues of all sorts, one might expect to isolate a large variety of yeasts from soil, which is true within limits. The yeast flora is controlled, however, by such factors as (1) longevity of a particular species, coupled with the ability to withstand local competitive soil organisms (fungi, bacteria, protozoa, nematodes, etc.), especially those producing antibiotics; (2) types of higher plants growing in the particular soil and the kinds of fruits or seeds they produce; (3) animals living and dying on a particular soil; and (4) soil composition, season, climate and temperature, sun exposure, depth under the surface, moisture content, and so on.

A great variety of yeasts has been isolated from soils by a number of investigators, starting with the early work by Emil Christian Hansen, and most recently by Lund, di Menna, and Capriotti. Yeasts are found in tropical soils as well as in those from arctic or antarctic regions. Only the more recent surveys have some quantitative value, since nearly all of the earlier yeast isolations were made by enrichment techniques. From what has been mentioned above, it is not surprising that highly variable results have been obtained. The total yeast count is usually very small, as compared to the numbers of bacteria and fungi present. Populations range from none or a few cells to several thousand per gram of soil from fields, meadows, gardens, forests, peat bogs, etc. Only in certain soils taken under berry bushes and fruit trees, which may deposit spoiled fruits with large numbers of yeast, have higher counts (of the order of 250,000 cells per gram) been recorded.

The yeast population is also affected by the depth in the soil. Yeasts are most numerous in the upper layers, from approximately 2 to 10 cm depth. In the deeper layers they become progressively scarcer and are exceedingly rare at a depth of 30 cm. Samples from the very top have very low counts if the surface is subject to intense sunlight, heating, and desiccation. The vertical distribution of yeasts in soil depends on such factors as compaction and porosity, rainfall, cultivation, burrowing animals, and on the presence and movement of soil-inhabiting insects which feed and breed on decomposing fruits (for example, the dried fruit beetle, *Carpophilus hemipterus*).

The maintance of a yeast population in a soil depends on

at least three factors: (a) regular replenishment of the flora by fruits, plant material, fleshy fungi, tree exudates, animal dung, and dying animals; (b) ability to multiply in the soil; and (c) the balance between death and growth rates.

In connection with these factors consideration should also be given to the production of yeast nutrients by other soil microorganisms. For example, bacteria and fungi can degrade substrates, such as cellulose and certain other polysaccharides, which are not utilizable by yeasts until they are depolymerized. This could explain why, in an experiment by Lund, soil yeasts inoculated into a sterilized soil had essentially died after six months, but in a control experiment with the same soil the natural yeast flora had increased greatly in the same period. A factor which has not been studied in any detail, but which undoubtedly plays a role, is the consumption of yeast by small soil-inhabiting animals, such as nematodes. It should also be kept in mind that replenishment of the soil flora with yeasts from plants and animals can be a selective process. For example, di Menna has clearly shown that the yeast flora found on pasture plants was taxonomically different in several respects from that of the soil below, even as shallow as one inch below the surface.

It would be going too far to list all of the yeasts which have been isolated from soil. It should be pointed out, however, that thus far species of some genera have been isolated exclusively from this source, although it could be that their true habitat is elsewhere. Examples are the species of *Lipomyces, Schwanniomyces, Kluyveromyces,* and *Schizoblastosporion.* Examples of specific members of other genera which have been obtained from soil are *Hansenula saturnus, H. californica, H. suaveolens, Candida humicola, C. scottii* (a psychrophilic yeast), *Cryptococcus terreus,* and certain other species of the last genus. A number of interesting new species of yeast described in recent years have so far been isolated exclusively from soil.

It is of considerable interest to know if potentially pathogenic yeasts are free-living and whether they occur in soil. Both *Candida albicans* and *Cryptococcus neoformans* have been found, the former by direct plating, but the latter only after enrichment by injecting a soil suspension intraperitoneally into mice. Neither yeast is very common in soil, and they are probably introduced via the feces of various wild and domestic animals. The occurrence of *Cr. neoformans* in avian droppings is a case in point.

YEASTS OCCURRING IN WATER

Yeasts are found in variable numbers both in fresh and in salt water. Our knowledge of aquatic yeasts is much more limited than that of the terrestrial yeasts. From what we have discussed in the previous sections and in particular that on soil yeasts, it is evident that waters obtain yeasts from a great number of sources. In the case of rivers, lakes, and coastal marine regions, considerable terrestrial contamination can be expected, and positive evidence in this direction has been obtained. On the other hand, yeasts can also originate from the aquatic fauna and flora characteristic of the environment, including plankton of the open oceans.

Yeasts from salt water. Surveys have shown that yeast populations are most dense in coastal waters, but they are also found in mid-ocean and even at depths of 4000 meters, although in small numbers. Population densities are undoubtedly contingent upon the availability of organic substrates for growth. Sea water normally contains between 10 and 100 yeasts per liter, but close to grass and algal beds, where decomposition is going on, the number of viable yeasts may be 5000 to 6000 per liter. On decomposing plankton and seaweeds the counts are much higher. The yeasts encountered in ocean water are generally asporogenous, oxidative types (species of *Candida, Rhodotorula, Cryptococcus,* and *Trichosporon*), which are not fundamentally different from the same species isolated from terrestrial sources. Among the sporogenous yeasts may be cited *Debaryomyces* and several species of the interesting genus *Metschnikowia.* The latter were obtained for the first time in pure culture by van Uden in 1961 from marine sources off the Southern California coast. A third species of this genus has recently been obtained from brine shrimp collected in a Canadian salt lake. Isolation of these species is of particular interest since they were described as early as 1884 by the Russian microbiologist Metschnikoff in their host *Daphnia magna,* but were not isolated in culture.

Fresh water. The knowledge of yeasts occurring in fresh water is very limited, but the available data again point to weakly fermentative or oxidative species of *Torulopsis, Candida, Rhodotorula,* and *Cryptococcus.* It would seem that studies of the yeasts occurring in lakes and streams and their characteristic fauna and flora could be highly rewarding.

IX / Yeast Spoilage of Foods and Fermentation Processes

Spoilage yeasts are defined as organisms which produce undesirable changes in foods or during fermentation processes. These changes may be limited to no more than an aesthetic alteration of the product by the physical presence of yeast. This may appear in the form of a pellicle or a turbidity in liquids, or as a slimy or powdery coating on solid products. Also involved may be changes due to metabolic activities of yeast, such as the formation of unnatural odors or flavors, and changes in pH due to utilization of organic acids. For example, lactic, citric, or acetic acids are used extensively as food preservatives, and their removal or reduction in concentration by yeasts can favor the development of spoilage bacteria. Fortunately, the presence of spoilage yeasts in foods has never resulted in food poisoning phenomena. The metabolic products of yeast are not considered toxic, and the yeasts themselves, even though some pathogenic species exist, are rarely, if ever, responsible for food poisonings as is the case with a number of bacterial species.

Yeasts responsible for food spoilage are often well-defined species. These so-called free-living organisms begin multiplying when the opportunity presents itself. The composition of a particular food strongly influences which species are favored in their development. From this point of view, therefore, spoilage of foods constitutes a special aspect of ecology. The selective conditions which are established by the chemical composition of the product, the manner in which it is packed, the temperature, and other factors of storage usually limit the number of species to a relatively few major ones. Even temperatures of 0° to 4°C, which are slightly lower than those found in most household refrigerators, do not protect products from incipient fermentation by yeast, provided the storage period is several weeks or longer.

We might briefly consider what the sources are of the yeasts which cause spoilage of foods. Naturally, this varies greatly with the product. Sound fruits and animal tissues are inherently sterile, but may become contaminated in processing plants from improperly cleaned equipment. Typical examples are wooden vats and cutting tables, pumps, pipelines, and other processing equipment. In addition, the outer surface of fruits carries yeasts, which were probably deposited by insects, dust, and wind. A few spoiled fruits in an otherwise sound lot can increase the microbial contamination tremendously. Finally, yeasts may enter by way of added ingredients such as salt, condiments, spices, and others. It should always be remembered that a few yeast cells can develop into astronomical proportions given enough time and the proper selective environmental conditions.

It is most convenient to discuss the spoilage of foods from the standpoint of broad categories in composition rather than to list particular spoilage yeasts which have been isolated from individual products at various times. In doing so we shall give some illustrations of typical causative organisms for particular kinds of products.

Yeasts occurring in substrates with a high sugar content. Such products include honey, jams, jellies, syrups, dried fruits, fruit juice concentrates, molasses, and other products preserved by high sugar concentrations. Yeasts that are able to grow in such an environment are usually referred to as osmophilic yeasts (yeasts which grow best in an environment of high osmotic pressure) or osmoduric yeasts (yeasts which can tolerate high sugar concentrations). We are speaking of sugar concentrations of 40–70% by weight. Yeasts are not easily inhibited by moderate sugar concentrations; at 40% sugar, a large percentage of the known species will grow well, and selectivity of the more osmophilic types occurs above 40%. In general, the higher the sugar concentration, the slower the rate of growth. There are only a very few organisms which can grow at sugar concentrations between 65–70%. Hence, spoilage in products of very high sugar content may become apparent only after many months of incubation or storage. Another factor which may favor the development of yeasts as spoilage organisms in solutions of high sugar content is their hygroscopicity in atmospheres of high relative humidity. This results in a surface layer slightly more dilute than the rest of the sugar solution, and yeast growth may well start in such thin films at the surface of the liquid.

Examples of yeasts which are recognized for their osmophilic properties are several haploid species of the genus *Saccharomyces,* particularly *S. mellis* and *S. rouxii.* These two species are most frequently responsible for spoilage in such substrates. A less common organism is *Schizosaccharomyces octosporus,* which was first found by Beijerinck in 1894 on spoiled currants from southern Europe. The authors have isolated this yeast repeatedly from the sugary coating which sometimes develops on the surface of dried figs and prunes. *Eremascus albus* is an obligate osmophilic yeast-like organism, which occasionally is isolated from concentrated products. Other examples are the so-called advanced, free-living species of *Hansenula*, as *H. anomala* and *H. subpelliculosa*, and the species of *Hanseniaspora*, one of which is appropriately called *Hanseniaspora osmophila*. Foods which have undergone spoilage by osmophilic yeasts are usually characterized by a slight odor of fermentation, caused by esters, aldehydes, and other volatile products of yeast metabolism. The yeast concentration is quite low as a rule.

Yeasts occurring in products of high salt content. Strangely enough, the osmotic pressure caused by high concentrations of sodium chloride does not favor the development of the same yeasts as are found in substrates of high sugar content. The development of yeasts in products of high salt content is characteristically associated with the production of fermented olives, cucumbers (pickles), cabbage (sauerkraut), etc. These products undergo a lactic acid fermentation after being covered with a brine solution. In the case of olives, a final concentration of about 6.5% salt is typical, but for cucumbers the salt concentration is considerably higher. Depending on the process, it ranges from 10–16%. During the lactic acid fermentation, which takes place at the expense of the natural sugar in the fruit, the pH drops. During this period a characteristic fermentative yeast flora also develops in the liquid. These subsurface fermentative yeasts consist of several species of *Torulopsis* (called *Brettanomyces* by some) and some species of *Saccharomyces* and *Hansenula*.

When the sugar is used up and the pH has dropped due to lactic acid production, a secondary, oxidative yeast flora develops at the surface of the liquid in the form of a thick, folded layer of yeast. This secondary surface flora consists of species of *Pichia* in brines of lower salt concentrations; also the imperfect yeast *Candida mycoderma* is very common. With higher salt concentrations, species of *Debaryomyces* become more prevalent. In fact, species of *Debaryomyces* are known to be the most salt-tolerant yeasts, being able to grow in nearly saturated brine solutions. Since *Debaryomyces* is a common yeast in ocean waters, it may well survive during the production of solar salt, and in this way arrive in brined products. Also in meat brines and in salted meat products the most common yeasts constitute species of this genus. The slimy films which develop with time on bacon, ham, wiener sausages, and pickled meats contain *Debaryomyces* in large numbers. In this connection natural casing in the form of animal gut is frequently preserved with crude rock salt; in these salted casings the authors have also demonstrated *Debaryomyces* species to be present in abundance.

Yeasts associated with products of low sugar content. Examples of such products are fresh fruits and unpasteurized fruit juices. In most of these the sugar content ranges from about 8 to 15 or 20% by weight. Many groups of investigators have studied the yeast flora of fermenting fresh fruits or fruit juices. A great number of species has been found, too many to be listed here. It might be mentioned, however, that quite characteristically *Torulopsis stellata, Pichia kluyveri,* and species of *Hanseniaspora* (including its imperfect genus *Kloeckera*) are extremely prevalent in such products. In this connection the very early stages of natural wine fermentations (in which surfur dioxide and pure culture inocula are not used) always show the presence of large numbers of these apiculate yeasts in addition to smaller numbers of *Saccharomyces, Torulopsis,* and *Candida* species. It is interesting that *Saccharomyces cerevisiae* is not common as a natural spoilage organism.

Yeasts associated with milk products. Since the sugar of milk is lactose, many of the spoilage yeasts in dairy products are lactose-fermenters, or at least yeasts which can utilize the sugar lactose as an energy source. *Saccharomyces lactis* and *S. fragilis* are two examples of yeasts able to ferment lactose. In addition, there are several species of *Candida* and *Torulopsis* which are able to do this. Because condensed milk is sweetened with sucrose (final concentration approximately 40–45%), non-lactose fermenting species of yeasts may be responsible for a gassy swelling of cans containing this product. Two species which have been found responsible for this defect are *Torulopsis lactis-condensi* and *T. globosa,* both of which are unusually tolerant to high concentrations of sugar.

Pink yeasts of the genus *Rhodotorula* are frequently present in milk and cream. Sour milk and cream sometimes develop red spots on the surface due to the growth of these aerobic, lactic acid-tolerant species of yeast.

Miscellaneous infections. Occasionally, uncommon yeast spoilage processes come to the attention of laboratories such as our own. An unusual case was a species of *Torulopsis* causing a gaseous spoilage in salad dressing. This mayonnaise-like salad dressing normally contains fermentable carbohydrates, in contrast to true mayonnaise, and is therefore more susceptible to spoilage. It has a high content of acetic acid, however, and the yeast which was isolated was found to have an unusual tolerance to this acid. In pure systems this yeast was able to grow in nutrient solutions in which the pH was lowered with acetic acid to 2.5. After about two weeks, evident gaseous fermentation had taken place, and this yeast caused active spoilage upon reinoculation of the commercial product. It might be added that most yeasts would already be strongly inhibited by acetic acid at a pH of 3.5.

The spoilage of pure fats and oils by yeast is rare, but products such as butter and margarine, which contain an aqueous phase in addition to a fat phase, are sometimes subject to yeast spoilage. Such yeasts—for example *Candida lipolytica*—possess potent lipases and can utilize fats as energy sources after hydrolyzing them to glycerol and fatty acids. This yeast has also been isolated from olives, another product with a high content of oil.

A limited number of yeasts form amylases and as a result can grow on starchy substrates and cause spoilage. *Endomycopsis fibuligera* is an example of such a yeast; it has been isolated a number of times from "chalky bread" and from macaroni or flour used for the production of this food. Some species of *Hansenula* can utilize starch, and these species are sometimes associated (although not necessarily as spoilage organisms) with oriental fermentations of rice.

Yeasts are also found as spoilage organisms in the wine, beer, and baker's yeast industries. In these industries, any yeast that is not the standardized cultured yeast used in the plant (it does not need to be a pure culture operation) and that gives rise to the production of off-flavors or unusual properties of the product is undesirable. A few examples may be listed.

Saccharomyces diastaticus, a beer spoilage organism, has the ability to ferment the dextrins in beer and causes the phenomenon of super-attenuation, giving rise to too much CO_2 and alcohol and leaving insufficient extract. Other yeasts, comprising certain species of *Saccharomyces,* are able to form higher alcohols from certain amino acids by the Ehrlich process (see Chapter VI). Tyrosol, formed from the amino acid tyrosine, has an intensely bitter flavor, whereas phenyl ethyl alcohol has a rose-like aroma and is formed from the amino acid phenylalanine. In the wine industry, species such as *Saccharomyces chevalieri* have been shown to cause turbidity in bottled, dry table wines (12–13% alcohol). Their effect is primarily limited to an unsightly appearance of the product. A similar case involves the growth of *Saccharomyces mellis* in sweet table wines of 18–20% alcohol and in sweet sauterne wines of 14% alcohol. Under these conditions the growth is slow and limited, but again it has a detrimental effect on the appearance of the wine.

The occurrence of "wild" yeasts with baker's yeast may lead to the more rapid multiplication of these contaminants during the production stages and to a decrease in the baking quality of this highly standardized product. The authors have had opportunity to observe the competitive behavior of *Candida utilis* (a well-known feed yeast) in a baker's yeast plant, where it had established itself as a contaminant. Since *Candida utilis* grows faster than baker's yeast, the final product, in spite of a very minor initial contamination, occasionally amounted to more than 10% of the final yeast crop. This particular contamination and competition could be conveniently studied by the fact that *Candida utilis* can utilize nitrate as a single nitrogen source, but *Saccharomyces cerevisiae* cannot do so. On differential media we could follow exactly the development of the contaminant in competition with baker's yeast.

Although many interesting cases of spoilage of foods by yeasts have been encountered and would be worthy of a more detailed discussion, the examples mentioned give the reader an insight into the diversity of yeasts as far as food spoilage organisms are concerned. Almost any kind of food will permit yeasts to grow, provided it has not been adequately heat-treated. High concentrations of sugar, salt, organic acids, the exclusion of air, refrigeration, and application of other storage conditions will not safeguard a food from the action of yeasts, provided storage is sufficiently long. The heavier the initial contamination, the sooner spoilage symptoms become apparent. For this reason, strict observance of sanitation in food-processing plants offers the best protection against losses due to microbial spoilage.

X / Industrial Uses of Yeast

In the limited space available, brief mention will be made of the ways in which yeast and its metabolic products have been made useful to man. As was explained in Chapter I, some of the activities of yeast have been used on an empirical basis for many centuries; nowadays, however, yeast is used in a variety of ways, often in well-equipped plants and under proper scientific control.

FERMENTED BEVERAGES

There are two broad classes of raw materials which serve as substrates for the production of fermented beverages. The first category contains a *natural* supply of fermentable sugars (principally fruits) and the second a *potential* source of fermentable sugars, principally in the form of starches (cereal grains). Since industrial yeasts cannot ferment starch and similar polysaccharides, methods have been developed for conversion of these polysaccharides into fermentable sugars.

Brewing. The main raw material in the brewing process is barley malt. Essentially, malt is made from special varieties of barley, which are allowed to undergo a limited germination process in special plants called malt houses. During this germination period, lasting from 5–7 days, the necessary starch-splitting enzymes and various other enzymes are formed in the grain. The malt is then dried to a low-moisture content at carefully controlled temperatures to preserve the enzymatic activity.

In the brewery the malt is crushed to a flour and exposed to warm water at approximately 60–70° C, during which starches are hydrolyzed to fermentable sugars, principally maltose and somewhat larger oligosaccharides. The process of converting starch to fermentable sugar is called "mashing" in the industry. Protein conversion to amino acids and peptides occurs mainly during the malting process and to a more limited extent during mashing. The soluble extract, or wort, is then filtered off from the spent grain and is pumped to the brew kettles, where it is boiled with hops to impart the characteristic bitter flavor of beer. The spent grain residue is a useful by-product and is sold as animal feed. The wort is then cooled, usually by heat exchangers, to a low temperature suitable for inoculation with brewer's yeast. Most beers are fermented by the so-called bottom fermentation process, or lager fermentation, in which strains of the yeast *Saccharomyces carlsbergensis* are used. The term "bottom fermentation" refers to the tendency of this yeast to remain suspended for a limited time in the fermenting liquid, after which it settles to the bottom. Fermentation is carried out at rather low temperatures, somewhere in the neighborhood of 10° C. The main fermentation, which lasts 5–7 days, is followed by a lagering, or resting, period of several additional weeks at a temperature close to 0° C. During this time fermentation goes to completion, and yeast cells, as well as proteins insoluble at low temperature, settle out. The beer is then ready for final filtration, carbonation, and bottling.

The other principal type of fermentation, top fermentation,

is conducted at higher temperatures, about 20–25°C, and is used mainly for the production of ales in Great Britain and Ireland. In this fermentation, strains of *Saccharomyces cerevisiae* are used, which tend to rise to the top of the fermenting liquid. Most of the yeast layer is skimmed off the surface when the fermentation is complete.

Because of its multiplication during fermentation, brewer's yeast is a by-product in the brewing industry, and the yeast may be used in animal-feed formulas because it is a valuable source of protein, amino acids, and vitamins. It is also used for therapeutic purposes in human nutrition. A disadvantage is the bitter flavor imparted by the hops, which is concentrated in the yeast cells. A debittering process, which involves washing the yeast in a weakly alkaline solution, can remove part of the bitter flavor.

Wine. The term wine refers to alcoholic beverages made by fermentation of the juice of fruits or berries. The juices of these fruits already contain fermentable sugars, and yeast can be used directly for the fermentation of the sugar into alcohol. Wine yeasts are strains of the species *Saccharomyces cerevisiae*, which are selected by different wineries for their suitability to the production of specific varieties of wine. Most wine is made from grapes. Grapes are harvested when they have reached the desired sugar and acid content and are then fed into a crusher, which crushes the berries and removes the stems. In the production of red wines the skins of dark grapes are allowed to remain in the fermentation tanks for a number of days and the alcohol formed is responsible for extracting the anthocyanin pigments from the skins into the wine. For white table wines the skins are separated at an early stage, usually after 5 to 8 hours. Fermentation is continued until all the sugar is used up, after which the wine is separated from yeast and other insoluble debris (called lees) and allowed to age.

The true sherry wines of Spain (especially in the region near Jerez de la Frontera) are fermented in a different way. Special strains of yeast are used which rise to the surface in partially filled barrels and form a continuous deck (film or "flor") after the sugar is completely fermented. This subsequent oxidative stage is responsible for imparting the characteristic sherry bouquet to the wine over a period of many months or even years. During its action the yeast lowers the acid content but increases the level of acetaldehyde in the wine.

Special fermentations. A number of special fermentations are used which are often characteristic of certain regions or countries of the world.

One of the most important products is sake, a Japanese rice wine which dates back to ancient times in the history of the Orient. The product, which contains approximately 15% alcohol, is made of rice. The rice starch is saccharified by a preparation called "koji." This material consists of rice inoculated with *Aspergillus oryzae,* a fungus producing the amylase enzymes needed to transform the starch to fermentable sugar. This step is accompanied or followed by yeast fermentation, converting the sugar to alcohol. The yeast has been termed *Saccharomyces sake,* but this species is now considered a special strain of *S. cerevisiae.*

In some countries mead is a popular drink which is made by diluting honey and allowing it to ferment by a suitable wine yeast. A small amount of diammonium phosphate is sometimes added as a yeast food since honey is rather low in yeast nutrients.

A number of unusual fermented beverages have been made for centuries in various countries; in some of these products bacteria and yeasts act together to produce the required end-product. One of these, the "Tibi" fermentation, has been studied in considerable detail. This popular Swiss drink is a sour, weakly alcoholic, carbonated liquid, made by the fermentation of a 15% cane sugar solution to which dried figs, raisins, and a little lemon juice have been added. The inoculation is done by adding a number of Tibi grains. These consist of a capsulated bacterium and a yeast which live symbiotically. The bacterium has been identified as *Betabacterium vermiforme* (presumably a slime-forming lactobacillus) and the yeast as *Saccharomyces intermedius*. The combined action produces lactic acid, alcohol, and CO_2. The Tibi grains multiply during fermentation and can be transferred to a subsequent batch. It appears very likely that the so-called "ginger beer plant," which has been used in England for similar purposes and was described by Ward in 1892, is identical with the "Tibi Konsortium." The so-called "tea fungus" is used in Indonesia to prepare an aromatic, slightly acid drink from tea infusion, to which 10% sugar has been added. Two symbionts make up the "fungus," *Acetobacter xylinum* (producing the acid) and *Saccharomycodes ludwigii*, a yeast which produces small amounts of CO_2 and alcohol. Other bacteria and yeasts appear to be associated with these two organisms. Another fermented tea beverage is "Teekwass" (Russia), in which a symbiosis between *Acetobacter xylinum* and *Schizosaccharomyces pombe* has been reported. A number of other fermented products are known where symbiosis between lactic acid bacteria and yeasts is involved. For the most part the responsible organisms have been studied only superficially and at a time when satisfactory methods of identification were not available. A thorough reinvestigation of these fermentations would be well worthwhile. Examples are Kefir fermentation (Caucasus), caused by inoculating Kefir grains into milk; Kumis (Asia); Leven (Egypt); and Mazun (Armenia.)

PRODUCTION OF ETHANOL BY YEAST

The industrial production of ethanol by yeast fermentation has had its ups and downs because of serious economic competition from alcohol produced by the petroleum industry. However, food and drug laws require that ethanol which is to be used for the fortification of beverages must be made by fermentation. This is one of the reasons why the fermentation alcohol industry is still in business. Strains of *Saccharomyces cerevisiae*, so-called distiller's yeasts, are used, and their selection is based on a rapid rate of growth in moderately high concentrations of alcohol. Yeast can ferment only hexose sugars and can convert these to ethanol (theoretically 51% by weight and carbon dioxide (theoretically 49% by weight).

Two principal substrates are being used. The first one is molasses, a by-product of the sugar industry, which contains primarily sucrose and some invert sugar. Fermentation of this substrate is relatively simple since about 90% of the sugars in molasses are fermentable by yeasts. The highly concentrated molasses is diluted with water to a sugar content of 14–18% and pumped directly into the fermenter. At the same time an actively fermenting starter culture is also added. Some nitrogen, in the form of ammonium ion, and other minerals are usually added to supplement the minerals already present in molasses. Both batch fermentations and continuous fermentations are used. In the batch process, fermentation is usually complete after 36–72 hours. It takes 2.3–2.7 gallons of black-strap molasses (cane sugar molasses) to produce 1 gallon of 190 proof (95%) alcohol.

The second major raw material is cereal grain. Since yeasts cannot ferment starch, the milled grain slurry is cooked to hydrate and gelatinize the starch, cooled, and supplied with a special type of distiller's barley malt which has a high diastatic (amylolytic) potency. The amylase enzymes of the malt hydrolyze the starch, at a temperature of 62–64° C, to fermentable sugars and low molecular weight dextrins. After sufficient conversion, the mash is cooled in heat exchangers to a temperature ranging between 21 and 32° C and inoculated with yeast. During fermentation additional conversion of the dextrins by residual enzymes occurs. To supply the yeast with nutrients, in addition to those supplied by the grain, about 20–25% stillage (the residue of the distillation columns) is added, which is very rich in vitamins, minerals, and nitrogenous substances. Fermentation is complete after approximately three days, and the liquid, still containing insoluble grain residue and yeast, is then taken to the stills for distillation and purification of the alcohol.

A number of other raw materials have been used occasionally. For example, wood wastes, such as sawdust, can be hydrolyzed by heating in the presence of strong acid, and the resulting hexose sugars can be fermented after neutralization of the acid. However, since wood is rich in pentose sugars, which cannot be fermented by yeasts, this raw material is not as suitable as that of the carbohydrates from grain.

GLYCEROL AND OTHER POLYHYDROXY ALCOHOLS

The formation of glycerol by wine yeasts and other species of *Saccharomyces* has been known for many years. Normally about 2–3% of the weight of the sugar fermented consists of this trihydric alcohol. Because of the great demand for glycerol during wartime, Neuberg developed two processes which greatly increased the yields of glycerol by strains of *Saccharomyces cerevisiae.* The normal alcoholic fermentation is often called Neuberg's "first form" of fermentation. His "second" and "third forms" are those in which steering agents (bisulfite or alkali) are used to divert the fermentation into different channels.

The function of bisulfite is its ability to combine with acetaldehyde, one of the last intermediary compounds in the scheme of alcoholic fermentation, and thus to interfere with its reduction to ethyl alcohol. The reduction now occurs with dihydroxyacetone phosphate as the substrate, an earlier intermediate in the scheme of alcoholic fermentation. The result is formation of glycerol phosphate which is followed by hydrolysis of the phosphate group and formation of free glycerol. Because of the toxicity of sulfite, the growing conditions are quite critical. A reducing sugar level of 20–22% and a free sulfite content of 3 to3.5% in a neutral medium has been found best. Such a medium can yield 27% glycerol on the basis of the sugar supplied. The difficulty is the recovery of glycerol (by vacuum distillation) from the fermented broth, which contains quite large amounts of salt.

Neuberg's third form of fermentation, or the alkaline fermentation, is based on the addition of high concentrations of sodium carbonate, giving an alkaline reaction. Under such conditions acetaldehyde undergoes a dismutation reaction, which is an oxidation-reduction resulting in 1 mole of acetate and 1 mole of alcohol from 2 moles of acetaldehyde. Again, acetaldehyde is prevented from being reduced by the hydrogen from reduced coenzymes, which in turn reduce dihydroxyacetone phosphate as explained above. With suitable strains of *Saccharomyces cerevisiae* (those that are adapted to alkaline conditions) 10–24% of the fermentable hexose sugar can be converted to glycerol. As in the case of sulfite, the recovery is very difficult in the presence of large amounts of sodium carbonate.

Of considerable interest is the discovery that many haploid, osmophilic (sugar-tolerant) species of *Saccharomyces* and related imperfect yeasts belonging to *Torulopsis* produce, in the absence of steering agents and under highly aerobic conditions, various combinations of glycerol, erythritol, D-arabitol, and sometimes D-mannitol. Under optimal conditions, as much as 40% of the glucose can be converted to polyhydric alcohols. Yeast species can be grouped by the products they produce. These categories include the following: only glycerol; only erythritol; only D-arabitol; erythritol plus D-arabitol; glycerol plus D-arabitol; or glycerol, D-arabitol, and erythritol. Thus by selecting the proper yeast one can produce almost any combination of these substances. The recovery of these products by distillation is much easier than from the alkaline or bisulfite fermentation of Neuberg as discussed above.

When once again microbial production of glycerol is considered economical, or if a greater market should develop for other polyhydric alcohols, use will undoubtedly be made of these haploid *Saccharomyces* or *Torulopsis* species, which lend themselves extremely well to this purpose.

BAKER'S YEAST

In the modern baker's yeast industry, specially selected strains of *Saccharomyces cerevisiae* are used. The product is available on the market in two forms: as a compressed yeast-cake of approximately 70% moisture content, and as active dry baker's yeast of approximately 7.5% moisture content.

Yeast has been used for many centuries for the leavening of bread. Prior to Pasteur's time, when the role of yeast in bread leavening was not clearly understood, the yeast was propagated from dough to dough or from mash to mash. Later, surplus distiller's yeast (after pressing out excess water) was commonly used. Brewer's yeast usually had inferior leavening powers and a bitter taste from the hops used in brewing.

Initially, baker's yeast was produced by growing it in a grain mash under conditions which were only moderately aerobic. As a result, yields of yeast were low and much alcohol was produced as a by-product. Four major fundamental discoveries are the basis of the modern yeast industry.

The first is the use of molasses instead of grains as the carbon source. This by-product of the sugar industry contains a very high concentration of utilizable sugar and, in addition, has certain growth factors and minerals. Secondly, the discovery was made that yeast can be grown with an inorganic source of nitrogen, added as ammonium sulfate and ammonium hydroxide, the latter for the purpose of balancing pH changes. Thirdly, based on the discovery of Pasteur that aeration inhibits alcohol formation, present-day fermentations are carried out with extremely efficient aeration so that alcohol production is almost completely suppressed. Fourthly, the use of feeding schedules allows the rate of substrate addition to follow the growth curve of the yeast. A low sugar concentration is maintained throughout the process, helping to suppress alcohol formation and greatly increasing the yield of yeast.

Baker's yeast is produced from pure cultures through many stages of increasing volume. Before the last stage is initiated in the largest fermentation tank, the yeast from the previous stage is concentrated by centrifugation in order to allow the use of a larger inoculum. After a sufficient degree of multiplication (usually three or four generations) has been reached, the supply of nitrogen is stopped, but aeration and carbohydrate addition are continued in order to "ripen" the yeast. During this period young buds mature and the yeast increases its content of reserve carbohydrates (mainly glycogen and the disaccharide trehalose). This ripening process results in a greater stability than if immature buds were present in the yeast. Finally, the product is harvested, washed in centrifuges, and pressed dry in filter presses; it is then extruded from a machine and packed in blocks of specified weight. These final procedures are all carried out at low temperatures, and the yeast is stored at approximately 0°C since it is quite susceptible to breakdown (autolysis) and to spoilage.

Because of the susceptibility of compressed yeast to spoilage, active dry yeast for baking has been developed over a period of years. Different strains of *Saccharomyces cerevisiae* are used, and the yeast is treated in its final growth stages so that the reserve carbohydrate content becomes very high. The harvested yeast is dried under very careful conditions, so that the sensitive enzymes responsible for fermentation are not damaged during the drying process. Smooth, round pellets of dried yeast are made from crumbled, compressed yeast in revolving steel drums through which warm air flows. Dried bakers yeast is also marketed in short strands of porous appearance. These are produced by drying on a slowly moving steel-mesh belt in an air stream. The yeast is dried to a critical moisture content of approximately 7.5%, because only at this moisture level can the yeast be easily rehydrated in the baking industry. In addition, it has been found that rehydration of the dried yeast must be done in water of about 43°C. Lower temperatures cause extensive leaching of the cell contents, and a loss in baking quality results. Active dry baker's yeast is of such high quality nowadays that its baking properties are nearly equivalent to those of compressed yeast. Moreover, the stability of active dry yeast is, of course, vastly superior to that of compressed yeast.

YEASTS IN FEEDING

Because vast areas of the world do not produce sufficient protein to feed its population effectively, much work has been devoted to attempts to supplement the available proteins with those of microorganisms. Because microorganisms can very rapidly convert inorganic nitrogen into amino acids and proteins, this approach holds considerable advantage over protein from higher animals or plants. In addition, microorganisms, especially yeasts, form a rich source of many of the B-group vitamins. Although yeast contains all of the essential amino acids needed by higher animals and man, the sulfur-containing amino acids, L-cysteine and L-methionine, occur in too low a concentration. For this reason microbial proteins are most effective as supplements (up to 50%) in animal diets rather than as the sole source of protein. Also, because of digestion problems, not all of the potentially available amino acids are utilizable by animals. The most widely used yeast is *Candida utilis (Torulopsis utilis,* or torula yeast), the proteins of which are quite valuable. For example, the lysine content in its protein is 70% available to chickens as compared to 100% for the pure amino acid. All evidence points to highly beneficial results when a limited fraction of the dietary protein is supplied by yeast.

Yeasts are produced from a variety of raw materials and by widely different processes. They are usually classified as secondary yeasts (by-products of the brewing and distilling industries) and primary yeasts (in which the process is designed to produce a particular yeast with high efficiency). Processes have been developed for growing primary yeasts on cane or beet molasses, hydrolyzed starch, acid-hydrolyzed wood, spent sulfite waste liquor of the paper industry, and various agricultural wastes. Well over a half-million tons of sugar, resulting from the production of paper products, is discarded in the United States annually. Aside from the fact that this is a serious disposal problem, it also forms an economic waste, since these carbohydrates can be converted into yeast. The suitability of *Candida utilis* for feed yeast production is due to its ability to convert not only hexose sugars but also pentose sugars into yeast protein. Furthermore, the yeast is easy to grow, since it does not require any vitamins or any other critical growth factors in these crude media. It is also fairly resistant to the rather high sulfite concentrations in sulfite waste liquor. The industry has been able to make a highly acceptable yeast product by growing *Candida utilis* on this raw material.

Feed yeasts are usually dried at high temperatures on steam-heated rollers, which kills the yeast and allows for better digestibility of the yeast proteins. In addition to torula yeast, dried brewer's yeast also has been used in large quantities to fortify animal feed formulas, especially as a substitute for dried skim milk powder.

LIPID MATERIALS

Some species of yeast produce remarkably high levels of lipid materials, which is quite evident when such yeasts are observed under the microscope. The cells contain one or more rather transparent, spherical fat globules of uneven size. They tend to cause light refraction as if they were small lenses, appearing quite bright in strong light.

Commercial production of lipid materials by yeasts has not been economical, except during periods of war. *Trichosporon pullulans* (synonym *Endomyces vernalis*), species of *Lipomyces* (one species formerly called *Torulopsis lipofera*), *Candida reukaufii, Oospora lactis,* and *Rhodotorula* species, are examples of yeasts which have been used experimentally or commercially for fat production. These organisms have primarily a respiratory, or oxidative, metabolism and they can convert carbohydrates to fat. The nutrient conditions must be such that protein synthesis is limited, as for example when the nitrogen or phosphate content of the medium is low. Under such conditions the crop of cells is not large, but the fat content is very high (up to 50–60% of the dry weight of the cells). Commercial production is done under compromise conditions, which results in a somewhat lower fat content but a higher crop. Often there is a growth phase in a rich medium, followed by a "fattening" phase in a nitrogen-deficient medium. More recently a yeast has been reported, called *Cryptococcus terricolus,* which produces high concentrations of fat regardless of the nitrogen content of the medium. The lipids include fats, fatty acids, phospholipids, and sterols. The bulk of the fatty acids are unsaturated, which is responsible for the fact that the fats are liquid. Ergosterol is the main sterol of yeast, comparable to cholesterol produced by animals. Extraction of the fats by fat solvents must be preceded by an acid or alkaline hydrolysis of the harvested cells if the solvents are to be effective. The fat coefficient, or the number of grams of fat produced from 100 grams of sugar, can be as high as 15 to 18 under suitable conditions.

VITAMIN PRODUCTION BY YEASTS

Many yeasts, among them most species of *Saccharomyces*, require one or more vitamins in media to supplement the nutrients which a yeast can synthesize itself. Other yeasts (for example, *Candida utilis* and *Hansenula anomala*) can synthesize all the necessary vitamins from simple precursors. *Saccharomyces cerevisiae* is able to concentrate and absorb quite large amounts of thiamine, nicotinic acid, and biotin from the medium of growth and thus form enriched products. By supplementing the medium with crude sources of these particular vitamins (or sometimes even their precursors) one can make yeast of exceptionally high vitamin content. Such products are sold for therapeutic purposes.

Baker's yeast, brewer's yeast, and *Candida utilis* are good sources of thiamine, riboflavin, pantothenic acid, nicotinic acid, pyridoxine, folic acid, biotin, para-aminobenzoic acid, inositol, and choline.

Some strains of the yeast-like organisms *Eremothecium ashbyi* and *Ashbya gossypii* can synthesize extremely large amounts of riboflavin. This property has been used to produce inexpensive, crude sources of riboflavin for incorporation in animal feed formulas. Yields are strongly increased by incorporation of complex organic constituents in the medium of growth. Under industrial conditions, yields of 4.5–5.0 grams of riboflavin per liter have been reported in 6 to 7 days of growth. With such high yields, microbial riboflavin can compete well with the synthetically produced vitamin.

Some of the sterols produced by yeast can be transformed, upon irradiation with ultraviolet light, into vitamin D_2 (calciferol). Some strains of *Saccharomyces* can produce 7–10% ergosterol on the dry weight basis, and such strains can be irradiated with ultraviolet light to produce a yeast of superior vitamin D content.

Although some strains of yeast belonging to the genus *Rhodotorula* can synthesize significant quantities of β-carotene, the concentration is too small to be economically important. Production of β-carotene by fungi belonging to the *Phycomycertes* is more promising than by yeasts.

YEASTS AS A SOURCE OF ENZYMES

Baker's yeast—*Saccharomyces cerevisiae*—is very rich in invertase, an enzyme which splits sucrose into a mixture of glucose and fructose (invert sugar). When grown on sucrose, this yeast may contain 50 to 100 times the amount of this enzyme needed to maintain fermentation at its maximal rate. Invertase is associated with the cell membrane and can be obtained in soluble form by treating the cells with toluene. Purified invertase is used in the production of artificial honey and invert sugar and in the manufacture of cream-center bonbons.

Another important enzyme which can be obtained from yeast is lactase. This can only be obtained from yeasts which can ferment the sugar lactose, and *Saccharomyces fragilis* is the most common source. Growing this yeast in the presence of lactose increases its lactase content considerably. A number of patents exist which deal with the production of lactase preparations from *Saccharomyces fragilis* on a commercial scale. These preparations are used primarily to hydrolyze lactose in milk products used for ice cream bases (to prevent crystallization of lactose), in frozen milk, concentrated milk, and animal feeds.

POLYSACCHARIDES

In recent years considerable interest has developed in the use of microbial polysaccharides for various industrial purposes, including their use as modifiers of texture and consistency in food products. Phosphomannans, which are produced by the more primitive species of the genus *Hansenula,* are among the most interesting and promising polysaccharides. These yeasts have the remarkable ability to convert up to 50% of the glucose in the medium to extracellular capsular polysaccharides, which are subsequently released into the medium. The polymers contain only mannose in addition to phosphate. Depending on the species of yeast producing this polysaccharide, the ratio between mannose and phosphate can vary from 2 to 3, up to 10 to 27 mannose units per phosphate unit. Isolated phosphomannans form highly viscous, clear solutions which are quite resistant to bacterial attack. They have been used experimentally for controlling the consistency of various foods.

XI / Yeast Classification

In order to report biological or biochemical properties of a yeast (or of any other living organism), a prime requisite for the microbiologist is the ability to recognize, identify, and name the organism with which he is concerned. To facilitate recognition of organisms by persons with different native tongues, every plant or animal or microbial taxon (taxonomic group) has an internationally recognized scientific name taken from the Latin (or latinized Greek). In contrast to many animals and plants, very few yeasts have vernacular names, such as baker's yeast (= *Saccharomyces cerevisiae*).

At present three independent international Codes of Nomenclature exist, namely for plants, animals, and bacteria. Yeasts fall under the Botanical rather than the Bacteriological Code. The Botanical Code prescribes that no fungus (or yeast) name can be recognized botanically, if published since January 1, 1935, unless a description in Latin is given. Names given without such a description are not validly published and have no standing. A second requirement is that the scientific name of a species consist of two parts—a binomial combination. The first component represents the name of the genus in which the species is included, while the second component is the specific epithet. Together they represent the name of the species. In the professional literature, names of yeasts should be followed (at least once in a publication) by the name or names of the investigator(s) who were responsible for the original description of the organism, and this in turn is followed by the date of publication, e.g. *Schizosaccharomyces octosporus* Beijerinck 1894. The purpose of this practice is to identify unequivocally the species and its authority. The Botanical Code contains many additional rules and recommendations, which are modified periodically during the various International Botanical Congresses. For further details the reader should consult the latest edition of *International Rules of Botanical Nomenclature*.

The basis on which species are separated from related ones is not uniform for sporogenous and asporogenous yeasts. In general, it may be said that for both types most attention is paid to physiological differences, such as the ability to ferment various sugars, and the assimilation of certain carbon compounds and of nitrate (the latter especially for asporogenous yeasts). In the differentiation of larger taxa (genera, families, orders, and classes) details of sexual and asexual reproduction, as well as cell morphology, play a much greater role than do physiologic properties.

It is well to point out that many controversies exist in viewpoints concerning biological taxonomy. Some investigators are "splitters"—those inclined to establish many species on the basis of relatively minor differences—and others are "lumpers," wishing to reduce the number of species. Species which have been validly published on a sound basis and which have an adequate description will remain in effect, although the higher taxon in which they were placed originally may be changed when new knowledge justifies such a decision. The specific epithet, however, remains the same, except for a possible change in the ending of the word to bring it into conformity with a change in gender of the generic name.

A few examples will illustrate the point. *Pichia membranae-faciens* Hansen 1888 was originally described as *Saccharomyces membranaefaciens* by Hansen, but was later transferred to the new genus *Pichia* by Hansen himself when it became desirable to exclude from the genus *Saccharomyces* yeasts which did not ferment significantly, and which formed surface pellicles in liquid media. *Saccharomyces apiculatus* Reess 1870 was changed to *Kloeckera apiculata* (Reess *emend.* Kloecker) Janke 1870. The latter designation signifies that Kloecker gave a more comprehensive definition of the species than Reess was able to do in 1870 and thus he amended the description. Janke, on the other hand, transferred the organism from the genus *Saccharomyces* to *Kloeckera* because ascospores were not formed, and the cells were apiculate (lemon-shaped) for the most part, rather than ellipsoidal. This transfer required a change in the ending of the specific epithet because *Saccharomyces* is a masculine noun and *Kloeckera* is feminine. Although Janke coined the name *Kloeckera* in 1928, the original date of discovery (1870) remains attached to the name of the species.

As in all other groups of living organisms, attempts are being made to classify yeasts into genera and families on the basis of natural relationships, thus taking into account the fact that yeasts (like higher plants and animals) have developed into their present state by evolutionary processes. Hence we have primitive species, in an evolutionary sense, which developed long ago, and more advanced species which developed more recently. A study of the development of lines of evolution in the case of higher plants and animals is dependent, in part, upon the discovery and study of fossil remains.

The simple structures of most microorganisms, unfortunately, do not lend themselves very well to a study of their fossil predecessors, even though these forms have been found in deposits of the oldest geologic eras. Instead, the evolutionary lines in yeast have been deduced for the most part from their associations with various primitive or advanced higher plants or animals (see Chapter VIII), and based on certain physiological properties. Much remains to be done in this area, and it is to be hoped that with the ever-increasing degree of knowledge and number of organisms studied, there will develop a much more solid foundation upon which to base a truly natural relationship between the different species and genera of yeast.

The brief introduction presented here will give the reader an insight into the problems facing the taxonomist. Nevertheless, the presently available taxonomic keys give the reasonably well-trained yeast worker much better tools in the identification of cultures isolated from various sources than was possible only thirty years ago. Improvements in these keys will make the task even easier. The present monograph must be limited to a listing of the principal features of the yeast genera recognized by most workers in the field. We are placing this information at the end in the form of an appendix, so those who encounter names of organisms in the text can orient themselves with respect to the features characterizing the genera in which these species have been placed. The arrangement of yeast genera differs in some details from other schemes, since it represents the views of the authors based on current knowledge.

In the case of the ascosporogenous yeasts, the presence of a sexual life-cycle permits a more reasonable grouping along "natural" lines than without this information. An arrangement of the genera into subfamilies is therefore presented where information permits it. In the case of the ballistospore-forming yeasts, where there is lack of agreement on the question of whether such spores are sexual or asexual in nature, a simplified classification is given. The asporogenous yeasts are placed, for convenience, in "form genera." Here it is recognized that some species may be placed in a single genus on the basis of similarities in cell morphology and of certain biochemical properties. If their sexual cycle were known, however, such species could be considered widely separated in their relationship.

Finally, in Appendix B, all of the genera of yeasts and closely related organisms are listed alphabetically in very brief form. This tabulation is to be considered as a glossary of the major features of the various genera. It is felt that the many examples cited in the monograph will be far more meaningful if the reader can rapidly orient himself by this guide. In Appendix A, however, the genera are listed by relationship rather than alphabetically.

Appendices Bibliography Glossary Index

Appendix A / A Listing of Yeast Genera and Diagnoses

(*m*) *Hanseniaspora*
(*n*) *Wickerhamia*
(*o*) *Saccharomycopsis*
(*p*) *Nadsonia*

5. Lipomycetoideae
(*a*) *Lipomyces*

6. Nematosporoideae
(*a*) *Nematospora*
(*b*) *Metschnikowia*
(*c*) *Coccidiascus*

BALLISTOSPOROGENOUS YEASTS

Family—Sporobolomycetaceae
(*a*) *Sporobolomyces*
(*b*) *Bullera*

ASPOROGENOUS YEASTS

Family—Cryptococcaceae
(*a*) *Cryptococcus*
(*b*) *Rhodotorula*
(*c*) *Pityrosporum*
(*d*) *Schizoblastosporion*
(*e*) *Kloeckera*
(*f*) *Trigonopsis*
(*g*) *Brettanomyces*
(*h*) *Torulopsis*
(*i*) *Candida*
(*j*) *Trichosporon*

YEAST-LIKE ORGANISMS

(*a*) *Pullularia*
(*b*) *Geotrichum*
(*c*) *Ashbya*
(*d*) *Eremothecium*
(*e*) *Taphrina*
(*f*) *Prototheca*

The last group of yeast-like organisms are "related" in some cases by their frequent association with yeasts in the environment, and by their superficial resemblance to yeasts in morphological and physiological properties.

While detailed descriptions of each of the genera are given in various other publications, brief descriptions will be given here which include the salient features distinguishing one from the other. In general, the description will include general character-istics of the vegetative structure (thallus), means of asexual repro-duction, characteristics of the sexual structures (if present), gen-eral physiological properties, and any special characteristics belonging to the genus.

ASCOSPOROGENOUS YEASTS

Eremascus: Species of this genus grow only as mycelium with cross-walls, but the mycelium does not disarticulate into arthro-spores. Thick-walled chlamydospores may be either terminal or intercalary. Sexual reproduction is between gametangia of similar sizes, which may originate from adjacent cells of the same hypha or from cells of neighboring hyphae. The gametangial tips may coil around each other. After fusion of the gametangial tips, a spheroid- to ovoid-shaped ascus arises, containing eight spheroidal to ellipsoidal ascospores. Occasionally asci may develop without apparent conjugation. Fermentative ability is lacking; growth in liquid media is in the form of a surface pellicle. Nitrate is not assimilated. Species of this genus are osmophilic and have been iso-lated from food products with high sugar contents.

Endomyces: The vegetative body is a septate, uninucleate myce-lium, reproducing by fission and by disarticulation into arthro-spores. Ascus formation generally occurs after the fusion of gametangia, which are not differentiated as to size. One to four spores are formed in the globose to ovoidal ascus. The spores, de-pending upon the species, may be hat-shaped, spheroidal, or ovoidal. Dissimilation is exclusively oxidative, and surface pellicles are formed in liquid media. Nitrate is not utilized.

Schizosaccharomyces: Cells are cylindrical, elongate, ovoid, or globose. In one species a limited true mycelium is formed. The cells reproduce by fission and disarticulation into arthrospores. Ascus formation follows conjugation between two vegetative cells (arthrospores). The zygote becomes the ascus; four to eight spheroidal or ellipsoidal spores are formed per ascus. Members of this genus are fermentative as well as oxidative. Nitrate is not assimilated. Two of the three species of this genus form a starch-like compound in the ascospore wall, demonstrable by iodine treatment.

Endomycopsis: Members of this genus produce abundant true mycelium with blastospores, pseudomycelium, and individual budding cells. There is occasionally disarticulation of the mycelium into arthrospores. Asci are formed terminally at the tips of hyphae or intercalarily, with or without previous conjugation. The spores, one to four per ascus, vary in shape and characteristics according to species. They may be spheroidal, ellipsoidal, hat-shaped, sickle-shaped, or Saturn-shaped. Members of the genus have mainly an oxidative metabolism, although, in addition, several species are weakly fermentative. Pellicle formation is often found in liquid media.

Saccharomyces: Vegetative cells may be globose, ovoid, ellipsoidal, or elongate. Cells are usually in pairs or in small clusters, but a pseudomycelium may be formed in some species. True mycelium is never present. Vegetative reproduction occurs by multilateral budding. In diploid species spores are produced directly in vegetative cells. In haploid species conjugation between two vegetative cells, or between a mother cell and its bud, immediately precedes ascus formation. One to four spheroidal spores are formed in each ascus. All species have a strongly fermentative as well as a respiratory metabolism. Pellicles are not formed in liquid media. Nitrate is not utilized.

Fabospora: Vegetatively, *Fabospora* species resemble those of *Saccharomyces.* They differ from *Saccharomyces* in that the ascospores are generally long-ellipsoidal to crescent- or kidney-shaped, although some species have spheroidal spores. Most, if not all, species will hybridize with one another, but they do not hybridize with *Saccharomyces* species. The ascospores are released as soon as the ascus is mature, whereas in *Saccharomyces* species asci do not rupture upon maturity; usually two to four spores per ascus.

Kluyveromyces: Vegetative cells are ovoid to elongate, reproducing by multilateral budding. Pseudomycelium may be formed. Ascus formation is generally preceded by isogamic or heterogamic conjugation. Asci may be multi-spored (more than 16 spores per ascus is considered multi-spored). The spore shape is ovoid to kidney-shaped. Fermentative as well as oxidative dissimilation occurs. A surface pellicle is formed by one of the two species *(K. polysporus)*. Nitrate is not utilized.

Schwanniomyces: Vegetative cells are spherical to ovoid in shape, reproducing by multilateral budding. Prior to ascus formation, the cell forms a protuberance (meiosis bud). One to two warty-walled spores with an equatorial ledge (resembling a walnut) are formed in the mother cell. Ascus formation is rarely accomplished by conjugation between two vegetative cells (isogamy). These yeasts are fermentative as well as oxidative in their dissimilation. Pellicles are not formed in liquid media. Nitrate is not assimilated.

Debaryomyces: Cells are generally spheroidal to globose, reproducing by multilateral budding. Pseudomycelium is normally absent. The ascus is formed by a kind of mother-daughter cell (heterogamic) conjugation, although isogamic conjugation between two individual similar cells may occur. One, or more rarely, two, warty-walled ascospores are formed. Dissimilation is oxidative in some species, but others have both a fermentative and an oxidative metabolism. Pellicle formation is variable. Nitrate is not assimilated, but some species can utilize nitrite. Most species have a high tolerance to sodium chloride.

Citeromyces: Members of this genus produce spheroidal to ovoidal vegetative cells, which reproduce by multilateral budding. No pseudomycelium is formed. Asci are formed from diploid cells. One, or more rarely, two, spheroidal, warty spores are formed per ascus. Spores are somewhat similar in appearance to those of *Debaryomyces.* Dissimilation is fermentative as well as oxidative. No pellicle is formed in liquid media. Nitrate is utilized.

Pichia: Cells range from short ellipsoidal to cylindrical, reproducing by multilateral budding. Pseudomycelium is generally formed but may be rudimentary or lacking. Some species may form true hyphae. Ascus formation occurs either directly in diploid cells or after a heterogamic or isogamic conjugation. One to four helmet-shaped, hat-shaped, or spheroidal spores are formed per ascus. A dry, dull pellicle is formed in some species, but it may be thin or lacking in others. Dissimilation is preferentially oxidative, but fermentation may occur in some species. Nitrate is not utilized.

Hansenula: Vegetative cells vary from spherical or ovoid to elongate and cylindrical. Reproduction occurs by multilateral budding. Pseudomycelium is commonly formed; however, it may be primitive or lacking. Some species form true hyphae. Ascus formation may or may not be immediately preceded by isogamic or heterogamic conjugation. One to four spores are formed per ascus. Spores may be Saturn-shaped to spheroidal or hat-shaped. A dull, dry pellicle may or may not be formed on liquid media. Some species are capable of a vigorous fermentation, although others ferment weakly or not at all. Nitrate is utilized.

Pachysolen: Ovoid, elongate to cylindrical cells, reproducing by multilateral budding. Pseudomycelium may be formed. A thin-walled ascus is formed at the tip of an elongated tube which develops from the mother cell. During the process of tube development the walls of the mother cell and of the tube become very thick. The protoplasmic contents go into the thin-walled tip of the tube, which develops into an ascus containing four hat-shaped spores. The spores are liberated from the ascus upon maturity. Species of this genus have a weakly fermentative ability, as well as an oxidative dissimilation. Nitrate is utilized, although its utilization is not strong.

Dekkera: Vegetative cells vary in shape from ovoid to ellipsoidal or elongate and are frequently ogival. Pseudomycelium is formed, although occasionally rudimentary. One to four spores are formed per ascus, which ruptures soon after maturation. Spores are hat-shaped to spheroidal with a tangential brim. Dissimilation is oxidative and fermentative (slow). There is usually a vigorous production of acetic acid from glucose under aerobic conditions.

Formation of surface pellicles is variable. Assimilation of nitrate is variable. This genus represents the perfect stage of the genus *Brettanomyces.*

Saccharomycodes: Cell shape is apiculate (lemon-shaped) or sausage-shaped. Vegetative reproduction is by bipolar budding on a somewhat broad base. Pseudomycelium, when formed, is poorly developed. Ascus formation occurs directly from a diploid cell. Four spheroidal spores are formed per ascus. Spores conjugate in pairs within the ascus. Dissimilation is fermentative as well as oxidative. Pellicles are not formed. Nitrate is not assimilated.

Hanseniaspora: Cells are apiculate or ellipsoidal to elongate, reproducing vegetatively by bipolar budding. Occasionally a primitive pseudomycelium may be formed. Ascospores are formed directly in diploid cells. Usually four hat- to helmet-shaped or one to two spheroidal spores are formed per ascus. Only the helmet-shaped spores are liberated from the ascus upon maturity. Fermentative as well as oxidative dissimilation occurs. Pellicles are not formed. Nitrate is not utilized.

Wickerhamia: The vegetative cells are apiculate, ovoid, or long-ovoid. They reproduce by polar budding on a broad base. Cells are separated from each other by a type of bud-fission. Pseudomycelium is rudimentary and primitively developed. The diploid vegetative cells are transformed into asci containing from one to 16 spores per ascus. The ascospores are cap-shaped; the crown deflects to one side of a sinuous brim giving the appearance of a sporting cap. Upon maturity the ascus splits transversely, liberating the spores. The single species of this genus is fermentative as well as oxidative in its dissimilation. A pellicle is not formed in liquid media. Nitrate is not assimilated.

Saccharomycopsis: Vegetative cells are elongate to cylindrical, reproducing by multilateral budding. A pseudomycelium is formed in liquid media. Vegetative growth of this organism occurs only between 35 and 40°C. An atmosphere enriched with carbon dioxide and a medium containing amino acids are required for growth. The large vegetative cells are short-lived when incubated at 35° to 40°C. Spore formation occurs in a diploid cell in which one to four ellipsoidal to elongate spores are formed. The ascospores have a double wall. In contrast to the temperature requirements for vegetative growth, ascospore formation occurs only at lower temperature (optimally at 18°C). The single species is weakly fermentative and does not produce a pellicle in liquid media.

Nadsonia: Vegetative cells are ellipsoidal, elongated, or sometimes lemon-shaped, reproducing asexually by a process intermediary between budding and fission. Short chains of elongate cells may be found. After a heterogamic conjugation between the mother cell and a bud, the contents of the zygote move into another bud (ascus) formed at the opposite end of the mother cell. The ascus is then delimited by a septum, and one, or more rarely two, spherical, brownish, spiny-walled spores are formed. Dissimilation is oxidative and fermentative. Dry, dull, creeping pellicles are formed in liquid media. Nitrate is not utilized.

Lipomyces: Generally, cells are spherical to ovoidal, with multilateral budding. Some strains, in addition, produce ovoid to cylindrical cells, often appearing in small clusters which reproduce by fission. The vegetative cells are surrounded by a slimy capsule. Pseudomycelium, if formed, is rudimentary. Asci are formed from vegetative cells as sac-like protuberances in which four to 16 (occasionally more) ellipsoidal, amber-colored spores are formed. Dissimilation is oxidative. Nitrate is not utilized. Under appropriate conditions large fat globules are present in the vegetative cells and a starch-like compound may be formed in the capsule.

Nematospora: Cells are spheroidal, ovoidal, elongate or irregular in shape (polymorphic) and reproduce by multilateral budding. A true mycelium with relatively few septa may be formed in older cultures. Pseudomycelial formations are always present. Asci are formed from a vegetative cell, which enlarges greatly prior to the formation of eight spindle- to needle-shaped ascospores. Each spore has a non-motile, whip-like appendage. Frequently the spores lie in two bundles of 4 spores each, at opposite ends of the ascus. Dissimilation is fermentative as well as oxidative. The single species does not form a surface pellicle. Nitrate is not utilized.

Metschnikowia: Vegetative cells are ovoid to elongate, budding multilaterally. True or pseudomycelium is not formed. The ascus originates from a vegetative cell. Prior to spore formation the vegetative cell elongates strikingly and assumes a club shape. Each ascus contains a single, needle-shaped spore without an appendage. Fermentation may or may not occur. Nitrate is not assimilated. Pellicle formation is variable.

Coccidiascus: The multilaterally budding cells have a spheroidal to ovoidal shape. No mycelium is formed. Ascus formation results from isogamic conjugation between two vegetative cells, and four fusiform spores without appendages are formed in each ascus. The single species of this genus has been observed within intestinal cells of *Drosophila funebris* but has not been cultivated on artificial media.

BALLISTOSPOROGENOUS YEASTS

Sporobolomyces: Cells are ovoidal to elongate, reproducing by multilateral budding. True mycelium is formed in some species. Pseudomycelium may also be found. Ballistospores are generally kidney- to sickle-shaped (asymmetric in form) and are produced on aerial sterigmata. They are forcibly discharged. Dissimilation is oxidative. Nearly all species appear red to salmon-pink due to the production of carotenoid pigments. In liquid media, mainly surface growth occurs. Nitrate utilization is variable.

Bullera: Cells are ovoidal to spheroidal in shape and reproduce by multilateral budding. True and pseudomycelium are absent. The ballistospores are typically symmetrical, being spheroidal to ovoidal in shape. They are forcibly discharged from aerial sterigmata. Dissimilation is strictly oxidative. In culture these organisms are colorless to pale yellow or cream-colored. In liquid media principally surface growth occurs. Nitrate is not utilized.

ASPOROGENOUS YEASTS

Cryptococcus: Cells are spherical, ovoidal, occasionally elongate, or irregularly shaped. Reproduction occurs by multilateral budding. Pseudomycelium is lacking. Cells are surrounded by a capsule, giving colonies a mucoid appearance. Growth on solid media may be pallid to somewhat yellowish or pinkish in tint, due to the synthesis of small amounts of carotenoid pigments. Starch-like compounds are formed on acidic media by all members of this genus. Fermentative ability is lacking in all species. Dry surface pellicles are not formed. Nitrate utilization is variable.

Rhodotorula: Cells are spheroidal, ellipsoidal, or elongate in shape, reproducing by multilateral budding. A more or less primitive pseudomycelium may occasionally be formed. Many species have a mucoid appearance due to formation of a capsule. Dissimilation is strictly oxidative. Distinct red or yellow carotenoid pigments are produced. Dry surface pellicles are not formed. Nitrate utilization varies with the species.

Pityrosporum: The shape of the vegetative cell is characteristically bottle-shaped or ovoidal. Vegetative reproduction occurs by budding at one of the poles on a very broad base (bud-fission), giving the vegetative cell a flask-like shape. Pseudomycelium or true mycelium is not formed. Dissimilation is strictly oxidative. Species of this genus do not grow well on malt extract media, but growth is stimulated by the addition of certain higher fatty acids. Habitat is on the skin of warm-blooded animals.

Schizoblastosporion: Cells are ellipsoidal to elongate, flask-shaped, and often polymorphic. Reproduction takes place by a combination of budding and fission. A pseudomycelium is not formed. Good growth occurs on malt agar without the addition of fat. Metabolism is strictly oxidative. Pellicle formation in liquid media varies between strains of the single recognized species. Nitrate is not utilized. Habitat is in soil.

Kloeckera: The vegetative cell shape is apiculate or ellipsoidal. Reproduction is by budding at the poles. Occasionally a primitive pseudomycelium is formed. Fermentative as well as oxidative dissimilation occurs. Pellicles are absent. Nitrate is not assimilated.

Trigonopsis: Cells are typically triangular or ellipsoidal in shape. In the triangular cells budding occurs at the apices of the angles, or multilaterally in the case of ellipsoidal cells. No pseudomycelium or true mycelium is formed. The single species of this genus is strictly oxidative. A thin surface pellicle may be formed. Nitrate is not utilized.

Brettanomyces: Vegetative cells are often ogival, ovoidal, or spheroidal; elongate cells also occur. Vegetative reproduction is by multilateral budding, often resulting in irregular chains of cells. Occasionally a primitive pseudomycelium is formed. Fermentative as well as oxidative dissimilation occurs. These organisms characteristically produce considerable amounts of acetic acid under aerobic conditions. Fermentation of malt extract is slow and gives rise to a characteristic aroma. Pellicle formation and nitrate assimilation are variable.

Torulopsis: Cells are generally spheroidal to ellipsoidal, or infrequently somewhat elongated. Reproduction is by multilateral budding. Pseudomycelium is not formed, although rarely a very primitive structure may be developed. Fermentative dissimilation is generally present, although in some species it is absent. A few species are mucoid due to the formation of capsules. The formation of starch-like compounds or the synthesis of red or yellow carotenoid pigments does not occur. Dry surface pellicles are not formed. Nitrate utilization is variable.

Candida: Vegetative cells range from spheroidal to cylindrical, reproducing by multilateral budding. Pseudomycelium is more or less abundantly formed, and in addition true mycelium may occur. The latter does not disarticulate into arthrospores. In certain species chlamydospores may be formed. Fermentative dissimilation may be strong, weak, or absent, depending on the species. Pellicle formation and nitrate assimilation are variable.

Trichosporon: Species are characterized by abundant development of pseudomycelium and true mycelium. The latter breaks up into arthrospores. Budding cells, occurring as blastospores on the pseudomycelium or on the mycelium, reproduce vegetatively by multilateral budding. Chlamydospores are formed by certain species. Dissimilation is mainly oxidative, although some species are weakly fermentative. Thick surface pellicles are formed. Nitrate utilization varies with the species.

RELATED YEAST-LIKE ORGANISMS

Pullularia (synonym *Dematium* or *Aureobasidium*): Members of this genus are commonly known as "black yeasts." They are found on plant materials and in soil and are frequently isolated with yeast. Most authorities recognize but a single species (*P. pullulans*) because of the numerous variations caused by genetic instability. The appearance of a young colony is from white or tan to light pink; upon aging, colonies turn greenish and finally black. Some strains, however, do not complete this color transformation. Colonies vary in texture from pasty or mucoidal to tough and leathery. The edge of the colony is strongly rhizoidal in appearance. Vegetative reproduction varies from mainly yeast-like (multilateral budding) to strongly mycelial. Arthrospores, chlamydospores, and blastoconidia are found commonly. Young vegetative cells are ellipsoidal to apiculate. Metabolism is oxidative.

Geotrichum: Members of this genus grow vegetatively as mycelium, which readily breaks up into arthrospores. Microscopic observation of such cultures frequently shows virtually all arthrospores and very few mycelial strands. Since this is a common fungus, of world-wide distribution and varied habitat, it frequently appears on yeast isolation plates. The colony is yeast-like when young; it develops rapidly into a white, spreading colony with chains of arthrospores, and shows dichotomous branching of the hyphae at the margin. A very weak fermentative ability may be observed, but the dissimilation is principally oxidative. Cultures appear to be genetically unstable.

Ashbya: This yeast-like organism is related to *Nematospora* by the shape of its spores. Differences are that *Ashbya* has no yeast-like budding cells and vegetatively has a sparsely septate, multinucleate mycelium. The spore sacs, which are probably not true asci but sporangia, are formed within the mycelium. They contain eight to 32 more or less curved, needle-like spores with appendages. Metabolism is strictly oxidative. Some strains produce large amounts of riboflavin in special media.

Eremothecium: This genus is very similar to *Ashbya,* differing primarily in the shape of the spores, which are short, arcuate (bowed at one end and pointed at the other), and lack an appendage. Dissimilation is strictly oxidative. Some strains produce large amounts of riboflavin in suitable media.

Taphrina: Species of this genus are parasitic molds on plants, causing a condition known as curly leaf. In culture they exist as multilaterally budding cells. Colonies are pasty, glistening, and often slightly pinkish in color. For these reasons *Taphrina* may easily be confused with typical yeasts. Dissimilation is oxidative, but surface pellicles are not formed.

Prototheca: Members of this genus are colorless algae, probably derived from the green alga *Chlorella.* The colorless, spherical to ellipsoidal cells may be mistaken for yeast cells. However, budding does not occur. Vegetative reproduction in *Prototheca* is by a partitioning of the cellular protoplasm into spore-like bodies (spherules). A mother cell with spherules resembles a yeast ascus superficially.

Appendix B / Principal Characteristics of the Yeast Genera Listed in Monograph

(The names are listed alphabetically for rapid orientation. The utilization of nitrate is indicated only if positive or variable, depending on the species)

Ashbya Sparsely septate, multinucleate mycelium; 8–32 needle-shaped spores with appendages occurring in groups in the mycelium; fermentation absent; some strains form large amounts of riboflavin.

Brettanomyces Cells ovoidal and ogival (pointed at one end), multilaterally budding; ascospores not formed; fermentation slow; a characteristic aroma is produced; aerobically, alcohol is oxidized to acetic acid; nitrate assimilation variable.

Bullera Multilaterally budding, ovoidal cells; symmetrical ballistospores are forcibly discharged; fermentation absent.

Candida Pseudomycelium, budding cells, sometimes true mycelium; arthrospores absent; ascospores not formed; fermentation and nitrate assimilation variable.

Citeromyces Ovoidal, multilaterally budding cells; 1 or 2 warty, spherical spores per ascus; fermentation positive; nitrate is assimilated.

Coccidiascus Ovoidal, multilaterally budding cells; 4 needle-shaped spores (without appendages) per ascus.

Has been observed in *Drosophila*, but has not been cultivated.

Cryptococcus Multilaterally budding cells of various shapes, often surrounded by a capsule; starch-like polysaccharides synthesized in suitable media; fermentation absent; ascospores not formed; nitrate assimilation variable.

Debaryomyces Spheroidal, multilaterally budding cells; 1 or 2 warty spores per ascus; fermentation variable; often a high tolerance to NaCl.

Dekkera This genus is the sporogenous equivalent of *Brettanomyces;* asci contain 1–4 hat-shaped or spherical spores.

Endomyces Septate mycelium and arthrospores; 1–4 spores per ascus; spores hat-shaped, or spherical (with a smooth or wrinkled membrane); fermentation absent.

Endomycopsis True mycelium, pseudomycelium, budding cells, rarely arthrospores; spores (1–4 per ascus) spherical, ellipsoidal, hat-shaped, sickle-shaped, or Saturn-shaped; fermentation variable, but weak if present.

Eremascus True mycelium with cross-walls, but no arthrospores; mold-like; 8 ovoidal ascospores per ascus; fermentation absent; tolerant to high sugar levels.

Eremothecium Septate mycelium; groups of numerous arcuate ascospores are found in the mycelium; fermentation absent; riboflavin is formed abundantly.

Fabospora Similar to *Saccharomyces;* however, the spores are usually kidney-shaped and sometimes spherical (1–4 per ascus); asci rupture when mature.

Geotrichum   Septate mycelium and arthrospores; mold-like; no ascospores are formed; spreading, white, powdery growth; fermentation absent or very weak.

Hanseniaspora   Lemon-shaped or ovoid cells; bipolar budding; asci contain either 2–4 hat-shaped spores or 1–2 spherical spores; fermentation positive.

Hansenula   Budding cells of various shapes, pseudomycelium, sometimes true mycelium; 2–4 hat-shaped or Saturn-shaped spores per ascus; fermentation variable; nitrate is assimilated.

Kloeckera   Lemon-shaped or ovoid cells; bipolar budding; ascospores not formed; fermentation positive; imperfect form of *Hanseniaspora.*

Kluyveromyces   Multilaterally budding ovoid cells; asci usually multispored; spores kidney-shaped to ovoid; fermentation positive.

Lipomyces   Capsulated, multilaterally budding cells of various shapes; 4–16 ovoid, amber-colored spores per ascus; fermentation absent; habitat soil.

Metschnikowia   Multilaterally budding, ovoid cells; asci club-shaped, containing a single needle-shaped spore without appendage; fermentation variable.

Nadsonia   Cells ovoid, lemon-shaped, or elongate; bipolar budding on a broad base (bud-fission); 1 or 2 brown, spherical, spiny spores per ascus; fermentation present.

Nematospora   Cells polymorphic; multilateral budding; sometimes true mycelium; asci large, containing 8 needle-shaped spores with whip-like appendages; fermentation positive; plant parasites.

Pachysolen   Ovoid to elongate budding cells; asci are formed at the tip of a thick-walled special structure; 4 hat-shaped spores per ascus; fermentation weak; nitrate is assimilated.

Pichia   Ovoid to elongate multilaterally budding cells; pseudomycelium variable; rarely true mycelium; 2–4 helmet- or hat-shaped spores per ascus; fermentation variable.

Pityrosporum   Cells oval or flask-shaped, reproducing by a combination of budding and fission; no ascospores; no fermentation; requires lipids for growth.

Pullularia   Budding cells, true mycelium, pseudomycelium, arthrospores; no ascospores; no fermentation; most strains become dark brown or black in culture.

Prototheca   Oval to spherical cells, which multiply by internal partitioning, forming two to numerous new cells; presumed to be colorless algae derived from *Chlorella*.

Rhodotorula   Multilaterally budding cells, usually ovoid to elongate; ascospores absent; fermentation absent; nitrate assimilation variable; pink carotenoid pigments present.

Saccharomyces Budding cells; 1–4 ovoid or spherical spores; ascus wall does not lyse upon maturity; fermentation strong.

Saccharomycodes Cells lemon-shaped, bipolar budding on a broad base; 4 spherical spores per ascus; the single species ferments.

Saccharomycopsis Budding cells large, elongate; 1–4 oval spores per ascus; the single species requires CO_2, amino acids, and 35–40°C for growth; fermentation weak.

Schizosaccharomyces	Cells elongate, reproducing by cross-wall formation; 4 or 8 spores per ascus; primitive mycelium in one species; fermentation positive.
Schizoblastosporion	Cells ovoidal or flask-shaped, reproducing by a combination of budding and fission; no ascospores; no fermentation; no requirement for lipids.
Schwanniomyces	Spheroidal budding cells; 1 or 2 walnut-shaped ascospores per ascus; meiosis buds often present; fermentation positive.
Sporobolomyces	Budding cells, true mycelium; asymmetrical ballistospores are forcibly discharged; fermentation absent; nitrate assimilation variable.
Taphrina	Multilaterally budding cells on artificial media; parasitic on plants, where mycelial growth occurs, producing 8-spored asci; no fermentation.
Torulopsis	Multilaterally budding cells; ascospores not formed; pseudomycelium absent; fermentation variable; nitrate assimilation variable; starch-like compounds not formed.
Trichosporon	True mycelium, arthrospores, pseudomycelium, and budding cells; no ascospores formed; fermentation absent or weak; nitrate assimilation variable.
Trigonopsis	Cells triangular (budding at the corners) or ellipsoidal; no ascospores formed; the single species does not ferment.
Wickerhamia	Cells lemon-shaped or ovoid, polar budding on a broad base; 1–16 cap-shaped ascospores per ascus; the single species is fermentative.

Selected Bibliography

BOOKS

Alexopoulos, C. J. 1962. *Introductory Mycology*. Art work by Sung Huang Sun. 2nd ed., John Wiley, New York.

Brock, T. D. 1961. *Milestones in Microbiology*. Prentice-Hall, Englewood Cliffs, N. J.

Condit, I. J. 1947. *The Fig*. Chronica Botanica, Waltham, Mass.

Dobell, C. 1932. *Antonie van Leeuwenhoek and His "Little Animals."* Staples Press, London.

Guilliermond, A. 1920. *The Yeasts* (trans. F. W. Tanner). John Wiley, New York.

Guilliermond, A. 1928. *Clef dichotomique pour la détermination des levures*. Librarie le François, Paris.

Harden, A. 1932. *Alcoholic Fermentation*, 4th ed. Longmans, Green, London.

Kudriavtsev, V. I. 1960. *Die Systematik der Hefen*. Akademie-Verlag, Berlin (originally published in Moscow in Russian, 1954).

Lindegren, C. C. 1949. *The Yeast Cell, Its Genetics and Cytology*. Educational Publishers, Inc. St. Louis, Missouri.

Lodder, J., and N. J. W. Kreger-van Rij. 1952. *The Yeasts—A Taxonomic Study*. North Holland Publishing Co., Amsterdam, The Netherlands.

Lund, A. 1954. *Studies on the Ecology of Yeasts*. Munksgaard, Copenhagen.

Prescott, S. C., and C. G. Dunn. 1959. *Industrial Microbiology*, 3rd ed. McGraw-Hill, New York.

Rose, A. H. 1961. *Industrial Microbiology*. Butterworths Inc., Washington, D.C.

Biochemistry of Industrial Micro-organisms. C. Rainbow and A. H. Rose, eds. Academic Press, New York.

Die Hefen, vol. I: *Die Hefen in der Wissenschaft*. 1960. F. Reiff, R. Kautzmann, H. Lüers, and M. Lindemann, eds. Verlag Hans Carl, Nürnberg, Germany.

Die Hefen, vol. II: *Technologie der Hefen*. 1962. F. Reiff, R. Kautzmann, H. Lüers, and M. Lindemann, eds. Verlag Hans Carl, Nürnberg, Germany.

Industrial Fermentations, vols. I and II. 1954. L. A. Underkofler and R. J. Hickey, eds. Chemical Publishing Co., New York.

Medical Mycology. 1954. R. D. G. Ph. Simons, ed. Elsevier Publishing Co., Amsterdam, The Netherlands.

The Chemistry and Biology of Yeasts. 1957. A. H. Cook, ed. Academic Press, New York.

REVIEWS AND OTHER SELECTED PUBLICATIONS

Hawthorne, D. C. and R. K. Mortimer. 1960. "Chromosome mapping in *Saccharomyces:* centromere-linked genes," *Genetics* 45, 1085–1110.

Joslyn, M. A. 1951. "Nutrient requirements of yeast." *Mycopathol. et Mycol. applicata 5,* 260–276.

Kluyver, A. J., J. P. van der Walt, and A. J. van Triet. 1953. "Pulcherrimin, the pigment of *Candida pulcherrima*," *Proc. Natl. Acad. Sciences* (Washington, D.C.) *39,* 583–593.

Lindegren, C. C. 1962. *Yeast Genetics*. Publication of the Biological Research Laboratory, Southern Illinois University, Carbondale, Ill.

MacDonald, J. C. 1965. "Biosynthesis of Pulcherriminic Acid," *Biochem. J., 96,* 533–538.

Miller, J. J., and O. Hoffmann-Ostenhof. 1964. "Spore formation and germination in *Saccharomyces*," *Zeitschr. f. Allg. Mikrobiologie 4,* 273–294.

Mrak, E. M., and H. J. Phaff. 1948. "Yeasts," *Ann. Rev. Microbiol. 2,* 1–46.

Nagai, S., N. Yanagishima, and H. Nagai. 1961. "Advances in the study of respiration-deficient (RD) mutation in yeast and other microorganisms," *Bacteriol. Rev. 25*, 404–426.

Nickerson, W. J. 1963. "Symposium on biochemical bases of morphogenesis in fungi. IV: Molecular basis of form in yeast," *Bacteriol. Rev. 27*, 305–324.

Phaff, H. J. 1963. "Cell wall of Yeasts," *Ann. Rev. Microbiol. 17*, 15–31.

Phaff, H. J. and E. M. Mrak. 1948–1949. "Sporulation in yeasts," Parts I and II. *Wallerstein Laboratory Communications 11*, 261–279, and *12*, 29–44.

Simpson, K. L., T. O. M. Nakayama, and C. O. Chichester. 1964. "Biosynthesis of yeast carotenoids," *J. Bacteriol. 88*, 1688–1694.

Skinner, C. E., and D. W. Fletcher. 1960. "A review of the genus *Candida*," *Bacteriol. Rev. 24*, 397–416.

Spencer, J. F. T., and H. R. Sallans. 1956. "Production of polyhydric alcohols by osmophilic yeasts," *Can. J. Microbiol. 2*, 72–79.

Tulloch, A. P., and J. F. T. Spencer. 1964. "Extracellular glycolipids of *Rhodotorula* species," *Can. J. Chem. 42*, 830–835.

Webb, A. D., and J. L. Ingraham. 1963. "Fusel Oil," *Advances Appl. Microbiol. 5*, 317–353.

Wickerham, L. J. 1951. "Taxonomy of Yeasts," *U. S. Dept. Agriculture, Techn. Bull. No.* 1029, 1–56.

Wickerham, L. J. 1952. "Recent advances in the taxonomy of yeasts," *Ann. Rev. Microbiol. 6*, 317–332.

Wickerham, L. J., and K. A. Burton. 1952. "Occurrence of yeast mating types in nature," *J. Bacteriol. 63*, 449–451.

Wickerham, L. J. and K. A. Burton. 1962. "Phylogeny and biochemistry of the genus *Hansenula*," *Bacteriol. Rev. 26*, 382–397.

Glossary of Certain Mycological Terms Used in the Text

Apiculate: A cell shape, somewhat resembling the form of a lemon; having protuberances at both ends of the long axis of the cell.

Arthrospore: A nonsexual spore resulting from the disarticulation of hyphae or of single cells dividing by cross-wall formation. Sometimes called oidium.

Ascospore: A sexual spore borne in an ascus.

Ascus (pl. asci): A sac-like structure containing the ascospores formed by certain yeasts.

Basidiospore: A sexual spore borne on the outside of a basidium, usually on a specialized structure of pointed shape called a sterigma.

Basidium (pl. basidia): A structure (typical of the class Basidiomycetes) in which nuclear fusion and reduction division occur, and which bears the externally located basidiospores.

Blastospore: A nonsexual reproductive cell formed by budding, normally near the apex of an elongated cell, or in the area where pseudomycelial cells are joined together.

Blastoconidium: An individual nonsexual reproductive cell formed by budding along a hyphal filament, but not located at the apex where elongated cells of a pseudomycelium are joined together, or at the septa of true hyphae.

Chlamydospore: A nonsexual resting cell, enveloped by a thick cell wall.

Conjugation: The fusion of two individual cells (gametes), usually followed by nuclear fusion and reduction division.

Conjugation Tube: A tube-like protuberance which is usually formed by each of the two gametes participating in the conjugation process. The tips of the conjugation tubes (which may be very short or long) fuse and grow together.

Dikaryotic: Binucleate condition; usually referring to a cell containing a pair of nuclei, each derived from a different parent.

Diploid: Containing twice the basic number of chromosomes (2n).

Diplophase: That part of the life cycle which represents the diploid condition.

Fission: A term used to designate an asexual reproductive process, in which a cell forms a cross-wall (septum) and is then separated into two cells along the cross-wall. This process is exemplified by members of the genus *Schizosaccharomyces*—the "fission yeasts."

Gametangium (pl. gametangia): A structure which contains gametes.

Gamete: A differentiated sex cell, or sex nucleus, which normally fuses with another in sexual reproduction.

Genus (pl. genera): A taxonomic category, or taxon, which is composed of one or more species. The generic name is the first word in a binomial designation of a species.

Haploid: Containing the basic (or reduced) number of chromosomes (1n).

Haplophase: That part of the life cycle which represents the haploid condition.

Heterogamous (also called heterogamic): Usually refers to morphologically different gametes; male and female gametes.

Heterothallic: Refers to fungi (or yeasts) in which the sexes are separated in separate thalli; thus, gametes from two different thalli are required for sexual reproduction.

Heterozygous: Refers to the diploid condition in which the nucleus is the result of the union of two dissimilar haploid nuclei.

Homothallic: Refers to yeasts in which sexual reproduction can take place with identical nuclei undergoing fusion.

Homozygous: Refers to a character or trait of a diploid yeast in which both of the contributing nuclei contain identical genes for that particular character.

Hypha (pl. hyphae): One of the tube-like or thread-like elements which make up the mycelial or pseudomycelial structure of a yeast or fungus.

Intercalary: Refers to a position (usually of a spore or ascus) within a hypha (as opposed to terminal).

Karyogamy: The fusion of two nuclei.

Meiosis: Reduction division of a nucleus during sexual reproduction (formation of ascospores). Reduction refers to a decrease in number of chromosomes per nucleus, e.g., from 2n to 1n.

Mitosis: Normal nuclear division with retention of the original number of chromosomes.

Mycelium (pl. mycelia): Also termed true mycelium in the literature on yeasts. A mass of true hyphae (usually with cross-walls) constituting the vegetative body or thallus of a yeast.

Ogival: A cell shape where one end of an elongated cell is pointed and the other end rounded.

Pellicle: A skin-like or film-like surface growth of a yeast.

Ploidy: Degree of ploidy refers to the number of basic sets of chromosomes (1n, 2n, 3n, etc.).

Pseudomycelium: A series of cells which remain attached to each other, forming branched chains. In contrast to true mycelium, the component cells originally arose by budding rather than by cross-wall formation. The component hyphae are usually termed pseudohyphae.

Septate: With cross-walls.

Septum (pl. septa): A cross-wall in a hypha.

Species (sing. and pl. species): Normally the lowest unit of classification. A group of related individuals which compose a genus. Species are designated by binomials consisting of the generic name (first word) followed by the specific epithet.

Sterigma (pl. sterigmata): A small stalk-like structure which supports a spore. In the case of yeasts it is the structure supporting the ballistospore formed by the *Sporobolomycetaceae*.

Thallus (pl. thalli): The vegetative body (somatic phase) of a yeast or fungus.

Zygote: The product of nuclear fusion. Also the cell or combination of two cells in which karyogamy has taken place.

Index